TIPS FOR TIME TRAVELLERS

TIPS FOR
TIME
TRAVELLERS

Visionary Insights into New Technology, Life
and the Future by one of the World's Leading
Technology Prophets

Peter Cochrane

ORION
BUSINESS
BOOKS

First published in Great Britain in 1997 by
Orion Business
An imprint of The Orion Publishing Group Ltd
Orion House, 5 Upper St Martin's Lane, London WC2H 9EA

A CIP catalogue record for this book
is available from the British Library.

ISBN: 0 75281 349 8

Typeset by Selwood Systems, Frome.

Printed in Great Britain by Butler & Tanner Ltd, Frome and London.

SPECIAL CREDITS – IMAGES & GRAPHICS

All the visual material used in this book was prepared by Gary Dalton, Andy
Gower, and Craig Cater of BT. Their primary objective was to illustrate specific
aspects of the text spanning: the visualisation of Fractals and Chaos; a
coalescing of people and electronics including the embedding of electronics
inside the human body; through to the creation of new interactive
technologies and working environments. In this endeavour they had access to
photographic materials created by Roger Merton and others at BT Laboratories.
This included personal appearances made by Keith Cameron and Karen Willis
who kindly gave their permission for me to use their images.

Many of the people images were also supplied under copyright by
Photodisc Europe Ltd, Regal House, 70 London Road, Twickenham TW1 3QS.

The medical images showing a Kappa* Pacemaker and a spinal pain relief
module were kindly supplied by Bill Bedor of Medtronic Inc., 7000 Central
Avenue, Minneapolis, Minnesota, 55432, USA.

To all of these people I owe a special thank you for their individual and team
contributions.

Peter Cochrane

The images reproduced in this book are subject to copyright and were printed
with the permission of:
Medtronic Inc., USA
Photodisc Europe Ltd, UK
BT Laboratories, UK

For tribal man space was the uncontrollable mystery. For technological man it is time that occupies the same role.

Marshall McLuhan, 1951

For Brenda, my closest and most trustworthy time traveller.

CONTENTS

Preface

CONTENTS

THANK YOU

Being the product of working with hundreds of people and meeting with thousands over my life to date, makes it impossible to name everyone I am indebted to; but I feel I should at least mention those directly involved in the most recent production process. John Browning of Wired UK and Robin Hunt of the Guardian Newspaper Group deserve a special mention for originally inviting me to write for them some 4 years ago. Ben Rooney my current editor at the *Daily Telegraph* has been another key player in encouraging me to write and be ultra-productive. I well remember him asking me to write a 1-year series of 52 monologues for Connected@Telegraph, and worrying about my ability to find even the first 10 topics to write about. However, once I got started, one topic after another just seemed to pop into my head, and Ben has never seen fit to significantly massage my drafts or change my messages; he has simply encouraged and gently steered the development of these articles from time to time.

Martin Liu of Orion Publishing cold-called me by e-mail one day in February 1997 and we had our first meeting in the Housemaster's office at St Dunstan's College in Catford, London just before I gave the 1997 Armstrong Society Lecture. From the outset he moved very quickly to reach an agreement, formulate a plan and kick the process of production into being. At this point my younger daughter Sarah took charge of me and made sure I did all the right things on time and in the right style. She also did quite a job as the proof reader, sub-editor, agent and manager.

Collectively I must also mention my 660-strong research team at BT Laboratories, the managers and people in BT the company, all my colleagues in academia, and the members of the CSC Vanguard Advisory Board. In one respect or another they have influenced and directed my thinking and productivity.

Without all these people this book would not be, and I would not have achieved so much so fast. To all of them, I afford a warm thank-you.

Peter Cochrane
Martlesham Heath, Ipswich, UK
August 1997

PREFACE

This may be the most unusual book you ever buy or read. The content, format, purpose and style are unconventional by design, to meet the needs of time travellers – us. It was written on planes, trains and in the back of cars as I travelled through time and space. Most of the content has appeared in a weekly column in the *Daily Telegraph* and other newspapers and magazines, plus radio and TV interviews worldwide. So you might well ask: why put it all in a book? Well, it is all part of an experiment in communication and meme propagation. Not everyone is on line; not everyone buys a newspaper, or watches TV, listens to the radio; paper is still a very user friendly technology, and part of a multimedia world.

Thirty years ago I could have found time to read *War and Peace* or any other tomb. Even 10 years ago I might have attempted such a laborious process, but not any more. I just cannot find the time to work through 10, 30-page (or more) chapters, let alone 2 or 3 chapters in one go. So this book is written and organised in subject bytes of about 600 words. These 24kbyte monologues can be read in less than 5 minutes while you wait for a cab, have lunch, a coffee, an Internet download, or perhaps more likely while you journey by car, train or plane. With the most adverse reading conditions and the busiest people in mind, the font, point and line spacing have been deliberately selected to minimise the need for good lighting and the onset of motion sickness.

This is a book for anyone interested, or concerned, about the future, and especially those ultra-busy people (time travellers) traversing the planet as atoms or bits to create wealth and transform society and life. All the content is drawn from the real-life experiences of someone living on the edge of the IT dream, an on-line human with a family, a full-time job, with responsibilities, enough real and virtual space and not enough time. In fact, someone trying to survive and cope with a world of exponential change, a lover of technology, people, and a hater of bad design and unfriendly interfaces.

The monologues are self-contained and can be read in any order. There seems to be no logical way to order the subject matter, so I made no effort to do so. However, the monologues are numbered M0, M1, etc. with an index (MIn) at the back to facilitate keyword search should you need to find relevant material or a route to meme linking.

When you have bought, read or sampled this book, you may wish to visit my home page to discover much more material and depth:

http://www.labs.bt.com/people/cochrap/

This collection of bytes is a product of meeting and working with people and technology in my parent organisation BT, as a consultant to industry and government, being an educator, and technology prophet. All have played an important part in shaping my thoughts and ideas as we have struggled to find solutions to problems and second guess progress. It is also a result of living during the 50 most exciting years the human race has seen. If I had the choice I would wind back my body clock by 30 years, take my brain with me, and continue my time travels even further than I shall be naturally allowed. For you the reader I hope to have pre-empted some of the changes you will experience very soon. Enjoy!

Everything that can be invented has been invented

Charles H Duell
US Commissioner of Patents, 1897

My grandfather was once heard to say that man would never fly; my father said we would never get to the moon; and I say to my children that I find it hard to conceive of any single barrier that will not be overcome given sufficient time and technology. After all, we have mastered conventional three-dimensional space – we can freely move anywhere anytime, even fly to the moon, and if we had the political will, well beyond.

Our true destiny lies in mastering time itself. I think we can safely assume that no one understands time; it remains one of the greatest, and perhaps the primary mystery for our species. As a measured quantity it slips through our fingers in a unilateral flow, never to be halted, never to be repeated, but at an accelerating rate as we age. None of us has enough time. A continual stream of technology has allowed successive generations to do and realise more than those who went before. For the generations alive today, and those to come, the process is moving into overdrive, and in danger of getting away from us.

My job, my life, and my mission is to live in the future, to be a pathfinder, at least 5 years ahead of any other human, and 10 years ahead of most. This role I have occupied for many years, living with, using, and being subject to, the latest technology emerging from my laboratory and those we collaborate with worldwide. So it seems to me, that in one sense I am a 'time traveller', as I have to flip between the old, new and 'you haven't seen it yet' worlds of work and play. Thinking up a title for this volume was therefore straightforward as I have chosen to record many of my experiences, thoughts and warnings for the future. In reality we are all time travellers, and this book records my first batch of tips for those yet to travel the same or similar paths.

Unlike the majority of science fiction writers, I do not anticipate technology leading to some cataclysm or apocalyptic end for humanity and planet earth. History is reassuring on that count. But, along with the opportunities for doing good, there are also dangers in a future that will be increasingly dominated by technology. Hopefully the 'tips' recorded here will help prompt the right thoughts and questions, and alert all time travellers to what is about to come.

He had decided to live forever or die in the attempt
Joseph Heller,
1961

If you were dying and all your mental faculties were complete, would you consent to the transferring of your mental awareness and capability into a computer? Most people I have asked say categorically no. Now, suppose the transfer was into an android with the ambulatory and tactile qualities of you, the real person. The majority of people still say no. But I would say yes to either extreme and everything in between.

I once asked my wife if she would still love me if I had to have a tin leg. She responded with an immediate 'yes'. She remained steadfast at the further prospect of a prosthetic arm, artificial heart, kidneys, pancreas, lungs, spleen, stomach and inner ear. But when I suggested artificial eyes, she responded with a resounding 'no', followed by, '*Just a minute, I am not having you dying by instalments.*'

The question I then posed, was: at what point are you going to say it is not me inhabiting an amalgam of flesh, blood, metal and electronics? Is it when we make the final step of transferring my biologically developed brain to an electronically manufactured brain?

For the most part these are questions people do not wish to contemplate. For me they are a rerun of a mind experiment some years after my father had died. Had the technology been available to capture his consciousness from his dying body, I think he would have said yes. However, my mother reacted vehemently against the very thought of transferring a loved one into a machine form. Interestingly, I would have done anything to have maintained contact with that intellect, that being who had initiated my life, nurtured, taught, and loved me from the moment I was born until we finally parted. His physical manifestation

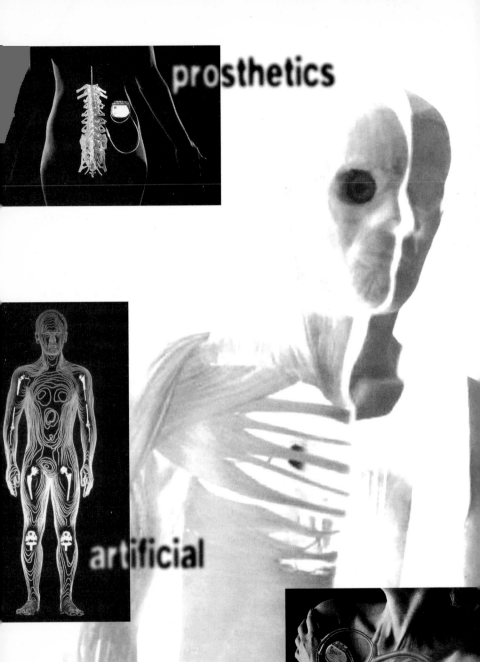

prosthetics

artificial

synthetic

mattered less to me than his presence. I would have done anything to have maintained contact with him in whatever form. For various reasons, I never had the courage to ask of him this question, and I will always wonder which decision he would have made. I suppose as I age, this question will be a recurring one and may even become pertinent, if not for me, then certainly for my son's son, or whoever. At some point in the future it is almost certain our technology will be able to transfer human minds into a silicon form.

At our present rate of progress, 20 years will see computers with an equivalent processing and storage capability to us, but this is just a start. Within 30 years the development of such machines should have reached our desk or pocket. Whether they will be capable of supporting new life forms, or imbibing existing ones, remains to be seen. The key challenge they will probably help us solve is the understanding of and access to the human mind itself. We do not understand how the human brain works as we have not yet unravelled its unbelievable complexity. Perversely, with future super-computers, it might be possible for us to create sufficiently good models to achieve a full understanding.

What kind of world will it be where no one ever has to die, or for that matter suffer unbearable sickness and failure of health? A world where we can live inside a static machine, communications network or inhabit some android or robotic form? The answer: a world totally different from anything we have experienced. Perhaps life and society will take on a new form, with the merging of intelligence and experience. We may even become civilised and stop slaughtering each other.

And still they
gazed, and still
the wonder grew,
that one small
head could carry
all he knew.
Oliver Goldsmith

Friday evenings usually see me going home exhausted with 8 hours' set aside for work at the weekend. But on the Saturday morning this work is completed in less than an hour. My head is no longer full; I'm no longer in overload and sleep has restored my energy and abilities. How come I am unable just to work flat out? What is this tiredness that my computer never suffers? It seems to be a combination of raw energy run-down and storage capacity overload. This can be accompanied by mild nausea brought on by a rapidly changing itinerary of people and topics, electronic and paper information I/O (Input/Output). I have reached my limit – and it is principally mental, not physical.

All biological organisms function as information processors; they take in information about their environment, process and use it to locate the necessary energy sources for survival. They are driven, therefore, by disorder (entropy, information) processing. The more efficiently organisms process and extract information from their environment, the more successfully they and their offspring continue their existence. Organisms are perpetuated at the expense of the less efficient – the smartest win. And so it seems to be in business and management.

The last two billion years of life have been driven by carbon-based molecular systems based on a combination of random mutation and natural selection. Homo sapiens arose through this molecular-based Darwinian evolution during the last 2 million years. And our future evolution depends on understanding that living creatures are information processors; that is, consumers of entropy rather than just energy. This implies that systems that are more efficient at information processing may one day supplant us. Indeed, for task-specific applications this is axiomatic and exemplified by autopilots, engine management systems and robotic mass production plants. But perhaps the difficulties the world chess champion Kasparov had with Deep Blue, and only a year later Deeper Blue, give a better barometer of progress. Only 10 years ago many believed such open-ended games as chess would always be beyond the limitations of computers, but no longer. Given the rate of computer hardware and artificial intelligence progress, even Deeper Blue will have Kasparov in even deeper trouble.

It is the ability of an organism, or organisation, to process information about its environment that is a driving force behind evolution. If there is evolutionary pressure to evolve better brains to survive, then genetic engineering and other biological options will not help if our brain is inherently limited by architecture and operational modes. The next step in 'evolution' would then be to appropriate silicon as the intelligence medium to augment our wetware (brain). Future evolution would then be driven by mechanisms and forces radically different from those manifestly of nature. Further Darwinian evolution could then lead to a creeping carbon-silicon mix.

At some point biological systems become inherently limited as they encounter fundamental physical limitations that constrain, direct or prevent further evolution in some direction. The most obvious examples are: the limitations on size imposed on insects by their ability to transport oxygen; or the stress limits of bone in land-based mammals dictating the leg thickness needed to support their weight. For us, it is the limitations to both our frame and brain. Having enjoyed 2 million years of encephalisation, we have hit the end stop – our brain gets no bigger.

If we as a species are to compete in a machine-dominated

culture, where are we going to find the necessary brain capacity? For certain, it will not be through the enhancement of our carbon-based wetware. We only have two choices: internal or external silicon extension.

The press,
the machine,
the railway, the
telegraph are
premises whose
thousand-year
conclusion no
one has yet dared
to draw.

Friedrich
Nietzsche,
1880

An ever-growing bulge in my jacket pocket recently prompted me to count the stack of plastic cards I now possess. These ranged from credit and bank, to security pass, vending, airline, hotel, insurance, health and retail. They numbered a surprising 27 in all. This further motivated me to investigate my cheque books, building society, health care, passport, driving licence, insurance and related documents, which totalled a further 23 items. My mind then turned to addresses. Home, office, telephone, e-mail, home page, national insurance, pension, and more revealed a further 32 items. Surely this is the wrong paradigm and it cannot last. Who wants to live this way?

Reflecting on the madness of a world awash with 21st-century technology embedded in 16th-century processes, the inconvenience of the train ticket, coinage and rubber stamp mentality also stood out. Consider the inconvenience. From passport control at airports to supermarkets, waiting and queuing is now endemic. Often the cost of waiting exceeds the cost of goods, or amounts to a substantial proportion of a total journey time. Just how much waiting time does a loaf of bread or an apple warrant? What is a reasonable proportion of the total cost? Well, most people get paid more than one apple a minute or a pack of sandwiches an hour. On this basis buying a house or a car is very efficient. But, drive 2 hours to the airport, arrive 2 hours early to check in, fly for 9 hours to the USA, and then spend over an hour waiting to get into the country because someone has to flick through the paper pages of your passport. Having confirmed it is you, your hand-crafted customs and immigration declarations are the final barrier to entry. Then, travel an hour to a hotel and spend 15 minutes checking in because they too have to get all your card details. Travel within the EEC and the proportion of wasted time is far greater by virtue of the shorter flight times. So – queuing exceeds goods.

Buying everything from socks to gasoline, it is the same. Information processing by humans is the limiting factor. What should we be doing? Well, a single chip on a smart card can now store all the above information and much more. Our medical records, insurance, passport, bank details and employment history could be written into the one device. Add a short-range wireless transmitter-receiver, and we have a personal transponder, just like an aircraft. We can be identified and information accessed or updated with no physical connection. So in principal, all our problems are over. Just wander into a store, collect what you want, swipe as you go, and we are the masters of our own delay. The world goes at our pace; we are in control.

Of course, there are worries about security. Suppose someone stole your card, or you lost it, or worse still the information on it was accessed electronically. Perhaps a PIN is insufficient protection, and anyway, with this sophistication who wants to keep punching buttons? Perhaps an electronic signet ring would do the trick. One thing is for sure: it could not be more insecure than the paper and plastic systems we use today.

Logically, a better scheme would be a chip implant. Just a small slice of silicon under the skin is all it would take for us to enjoy the freedom of no cards, passports, or keys. Put your hand out to the car door, computer terminal, the food you wish to purchase, and you would be instantly recognised and be dealt with efficiently. Think about it: total freedom; no more plastic.

I have experienced public discussions of cloning by religious leaders and it has not been edifying Richard Dawkins, 1997

There was a time when we could be educated for life in our first 22 years. For the rest of our existence we could gracefully get out of step with progress and complain increasingly about the changing world as we approached a grumpy death. But not any more; the world is moving too fast, and we have to keep up in an exponential race with technology. Our growing dependence on technology is, and always has been, irreversible; there is no going back without paying a terrible price. Everything we consume is created, organised and delivered by machines and networks. There are now too many people and not enough rabbits and berries to support the populace. Without modern technology most of us would die. How strange, then, that we live in a society where technological ignorance is so often lauded and even celebrated. But the people who deny technology are not only an impediment to progress and rational decision-making; they are a risk to all about them. Invoking superstitious or emotional reactions to apparently complex situations can be both expensive and dangerous. We all have a responsibility to keep on top of change, to keep educated. We can no longer afford to opt out, because there is no escape.

When faced with death, or the prospect of a seriously degraded quality of life, even the most ardent technophobes and anti-vivisectionists do not refuse an artificial implant. At this point replacement hearts, lungs, livers and kidneys rescued from other humans are no longer an issue or big news. Even piece parts from animals, or those created in any artificial or mechanical way, are gratefully received, while still being emotive headline material. The reality is that despite professed reservations, the immediacy of death prompts the vast majority to opt for lifesaving technology, no matter what its origins. It is not too difficult, therefore, to envisage a creeping evolution towards a cyborg world of partially artificial people. It already looks as though some 30% of our bodies can be replaced, artificially repaired or modified to advantage.

If asked to choose between a human or robotic surgeon, a joint of pork or beef, coal or atomic power generation, most would make the wrong decision. And yet robotic surgeons can achieve orders of magnitude more precision than any human; eating beef is far less risky than crossing the road; and burning coal does untold damage to us and the planet. People get alarmed at the prospect of silicon implants for humans, while happily putting their names down for silicone implants. On the one hand the material is inert and safe, and on the other there are very definite risks. So our society debates for some ideal physical perfection of form, and against the potential to repair damaged human beings. It seems political correctness and ignorance are now more powerful forces in the decision process than logic and understanding.

On the basis of such wisdom we now see beneficial research restricted and curtailed, as the new species, Homo ludditus, emerges with a call to stop progress. This has to be the most dangerous move of all. Do we really want to slide back to the dark ages when fear and mystery of the unknown ruled our lives? Or do we want to understand more so we can make wise decisions? To progress as a species we need our society to be better educated, and to have a more symbiotic relationship with technology. It is vital that more people understand the fundamentals. Not to do so will see us relegated to a second-rate and disabled species.

The agent just takes ten per cent of your life.
Raymond Chandler, 1952

In our real world we have become conditioned to all manner of agents. Examples include insurance and banking, police and state, sellers of property, company, security, and of course the secret agent. There are also rafts of abstract and less visible agents at work in chemical processes, medicine, biology, cookery, farming and much more. In almost every case these agents have beneficial properties and are used for good. Occasionally the temptation to become more efficient at killing and maiming prompts us to create defoliants and other agents of damage and death. So we cannot assume all agents are good; they are not, but mostly because we are the controlling agent.

Recent developments in our electronic world have seen much excitement among those working on software agents. In this virtual world we can look forward to new forms of agent that will search out information, manage vast networks of technology, and even organise our daily lives. Their intelligence can be expected to progress to the point when they will be able to negotiate IT services, software application upgrades and modifications. In a relatively short time we may see them scheduling journeys, buying and selling commodities, thereby relieving us of a considerable amount of mundane work.

Managing complex systems, resources and workloads should be the forte of agent technologies. They are born of an era of chaos, and they are ideally suited to deal with it. To date we see modest levels of agent intelligence doing increasingly complex tasks well beyond the established routes created by conventional software. Experiments are also underway to create systems that allow agents to breed, taking advantage of the best attributes created through a continual genetic exchange and chance mutation. Such technology should, in theory, be capable of keeping up with us as we adapt and adopt new technologies and working practices.

Now the obvious question arises: will all electronic agents be good? This seems unlikely looking at our history of bending good technology to malicious purpose. Someone is bound to create bad agents – spies and wreckers of systems. In fact anything we have already done in the physical world is likely to be emulated and exceeded. Someone, some organisation or group, is just bound to seize this opportunity to bomb, extort and manipulate this technology to advantage. But is there more?

For the first time the agents we deal with will have the ability to mutate and develop beyond human imagination. They may assume the proportions of medieval diseases to disfunctionalise individuals, organisations and society. Their evolutionary rate will exceed that of biological systems, and their host will be every computer and network on the planet. Every disc and chip will be a potential hiding place and incubator.

Should we be panicking or trying to stop these developments now? Probably not. For one, this technology is such a power for good, and for another, it is unstoppable. Someone, somewhere, will do it anyway. We have to be first, build and understand all its facets before the hands of evil have a chance to make a move.

We have the ability to create good agents that can combat the bad. A very fast conversation at their first meeting will reveal the purpose and intent. Good can compare notes and learn from each other as can the bad. But the overwhelming balance has to be good; just like society itself, it is a necessary condition, otherwise the system would collapse. A network immune system, complete with white agents (cells) could combat almost any attack provided it is big enough to surround and smother the offending entities.

If it can hold an
electronic charge
it can hold a
fiscal charge.
Kevin Kelly,
1996

For aeons we have taken raw materials and shaped them into artefacts we could barter. Physical articles have been dominant in the market place, with money the vital lubricant of commerce. Now we face a new and ethereal market: a world of bits, not raw material. While manufacturing bits can be very expensive, their replication, storage, transportation and selling are not. Here computers, networks and terminals replace warehouses, trucks, wholesalers and shops, to distribute faster and sell far more.

Macro-economies based on micro-prices are becoming significant as more software and services are sold on CD or on-line. Classic books, reference works and interactive multimedia entertainment packages are available with over 25,000 CD titles now on sale for a few tens of pounds. The complete works of William Shakespeare cost only 5p on a CD along with 2000 other works. Many soft products can also be purchased on-line direct from manufacturers worldwide. Even travel services, furniture, clothing and food are available on-line. This is creating a future of micro-money and macro-economies. The new on-line companies will see some remarkable new phenomenon as people buy and discard products faster, markets become more fickle and competition more transient. In this new world companies are likely to be created, come to dominate, and then die faster, as the economic cycle also speeds up.

These new industries will require new forms of commerce – new ways to charge and pay – in a far faster world of much more for much less. Banks will have to become electronic databases with no human intervention as cheques and coinage are uneconomic for such small transactions. It is also clear that anyone with a PC and a modest programming capability could open their own bank. Car manufacturers, supermarket chains and telephone operating companies have already moved into banking and financial services. Perhaps software suppliers will do the same and make enormous savings by becoming the distributor, wholesaler, retailer, and banker. One computer company recently put its sales and marketing catalogue on-line and now deals with 1.7 million enquiries a week.

All of this will erode the traditional banking sector and be compounded by a disappearing commodity – coinage. It seems remarkable that metallic and paper tokens (money) are still used in a world of information technology and electronics. Credit cards, electronic cash cards, the electronic purse are already in everyday use. In this information world, no money is exchanged; databases are merely updated. There is no gold, nor any need for it; it is a moribund concept. In a sense, geography is also dead and for the customer the choice will increasingly become stark. You can still travel into town, with all the inconvenience and time wasting it entails, and pay the additional overhead of a shop, wholesaler and distribution chain. Alternatively, you can go direct to a manufacturer in the USA, make a purchase and have your software delivered on-line at a fraction of the price, bypassing the tax system of 2 countries. At the same time the database of only 2 banks, customer and producer, change negligibly. No middle men, no non-value-add links in the chain.

We can now see banking as just information transactions. In 20 years we may look back with wry humour at those who currently argue for regional currencies bearing the profile of the head of state. Such concepts are likely to have been assigned to museums as the obvious alternative, bits, take over. The world economy is being transformed by IT and by 2015 some coinage and paper money might remain, and perhaps even a few cheques, but I'd bank on IT.

Communication, information processing and storage on planet earth, is now dominated by the digital computer. So it might seem curious to imagine computers conversing with each other through spoken English instead of their natural binary mode. How slow it would be – apparently pointless and potentially frustrating. After all, digital communication is millions of times faster, and more precise, than any analogue human tongue. And yet, in a recent experiment a text-to-speech system successfully interacted with a speech-to-text converter. Both were PC-based with a humanised voice and adaptive digital speech recognition. The remarkable outcome of this experiment was the apparent ease with which these machines could communicate without error. They seemed at least as good as some human subjects, and even in a noisy room they coped well. Most surprising of all, they could also converse over a standard telephone line. In fact, the more they practised the better they rapidly became – even more so than human subjects.

Could it be that digital machines are so invariant, their utterances so absolute, prescriptive and precise, that they are superior to our own? For us, every analogue utterance of the same sentence, word or sound is subtly different, and to make things worse, we use this variability to convey emotion and meaning. This is further compounded by the fact that we often do not say what we mean, or mean what we say. We also have a habit of creating a wide range of words and sentences meaning the same, or very similar things. In contrast, machines employ, and tolerate, far less redundancy. Our variability is a major limiter to concise and accurate communication between ourselves, and worse, with machines. On the other hand it is also a mark of our extraor-

avatar

Spaceboy - Photographer: good idea!

Filibuster the photographer: im shu

The
eze

Communication

John: Good evening, ladies and gent
Mass me
r
Anti-ch
democratic

interaction

dinary abilities and richness of culture. We are definitely subtle communicators, and in many respects well ahead of machines – for now.

So here comes a new and exciting paradigm with mankind and machine ultimately conversing on an apparently common level. Today we can only do simple things like find a telephone number or purchase goods. But it is a start, and voice interaction with machines will gradually become commonplace, giving rise to new environments, services, applications and problem sets.

We may only be a short way off voice command and interaction with all electrical appliances as a dominant mode over the button, knob, keyboard and mouse. Talking to your car, television, radio, home, and computer is all increasingly possible. Voice announcements, messaging, e-mail, text-to-speech and speech-to-text are already with us in trial services and some commercial products. Their great advantage is we can choose and adapt the communication mode to meet our individual skills and requirements. Driving a car while using a mobile phone, navigator or computer is difficult, dangerous, and illegal. However, talking to such devices is easy and safe.

Several machines joining groups of humans in conversation may also seem a strange concept today, but once we can converse with them, it will just happen. I will bring my semi-sentient machine to meetings with me, and so will others. So when two or more machines are present, will they talk in a human tongue or binary? For our sake it has to be a human tongue, at least during the period when we need to be in the loop of knowing. Interestingly, there will be a new silico-duplicity as the machines converse behind our backs, invisibly shifting Mbytes, negotiating, arranging and dealing to our mutual benefit. But their biggest contribution may be to refine our language, and improve our accuracy and efficiency.

It takes a long time to become young
Pablo Picasso

In a recent experiment I laid out 10 top end computers with CD capability and observed 200 senior managers and how they interacted. The vast majority just looked and only a very few plucked up courage to sit down and play. But to a man and woman all of them displayed one common trait: they pulled up a chair, sat down, and asked, 'What do I do?' Interestingly the same experiment run with children of 5 years old did not invoke the same response. None of the children would just watch; all of them wanted hands-on, and none of them asked, 'What do I do?' They just did.

Having studied this phenomenon further I discovered an interesting statistic. If you are 10 years old or less, the chances are you have had at least the same amount of computer flying hours as someone who is 50 or more. At 5 and below you have no fear, in part because you have not paid for the machine and the thought of breaking it does not pose a threat. It is even unlikely to be a conscious thought. If you are 50 or above, and you have purchased the machine, you come with a mindset that says: a £1000 expenditure is serious folding money and I'd better be careful I don't damage the machine. You are automatically inhibited and, in many cases, somewhat overawed by the technology itself – you reach for the handbook. Children seldom use handbooks; they live in a 'crash and burn' world of trial and error and, more reassuringly, talking to their peer group, exchanging ideas and experience; they learn by doing.

It is also interesting to reflect that if you are 50 years old, you are more likely to be extremely busy, finding it difficult to sit down and familiarise yourself with technology and simply play. Moreover, you are fast running out of lifetime years to do this effectively. In contrast, at 10 years old you come equipped with a mindset that assumes you will dominate the technology. You also have an abundance of spare time and lifetime years in which to familiarise yourself and become competent. In short, 50-year-olds will never be able to keep up with the 10-year-olds; they will be overtaken. We now have the situation where the generation gap is manifest in a 40-year lack of experience. So the people with the technological understanding and capability find decisions imposed upon them by people 40 years older with only a fraction of the capability.

Exposure to computers and related technologies is occurring at an earlier and earlier stage of life. The simplest teaching machines can now be bought for a few tens of pounds, and include voice synthesis, simple pictures and a good deal of interactivity. For many children the education and experience build-up for the information world starts before they are 1 year old. It is acquired in the same way that we learn to throw, write, walk and eat. It is not an adjunct, something special, or something that is taught as a subject. It is subsumed like language and becomes completely intuitive. Not surprising, then, that these children at the age of 5 are feeling very comfortable with the technology and by the age of 10 are undeniably skilled and capable people. What chance, then, the 50-year-old? Who knows? Perhaps we will be able to look forward to a sunset period of our lives where responsibility is subsumed earlier down the age structure so that we can have time to play too. One thing is for sure: we will see more 5-year-old consultants.

Twenty years ago we were all getting very excited at the prospect of the paperless office. What happened? We now use more paper than ever before and for many it still seems something of a dream. Relatively speaking, only a few organisations can claim to have totally changed the way they work and become so embedded in IT that paper is now hardly ever used. But in reality far more work and information is now processed and stored by computers than on paper.

The principal mistake made over the past decades was to take the paradigm of the paper-based office and put it directly onto the screen – and then back it all up with paper copies. Computer screens invoke, and allow, a different way of working, a new mode of operation that can now be seen as an entirely different environment. So after 20 years of exploration and wandering in the wilderness, the paperless office starts to arrive – today. Companies and individuals are now moving hard onto the screen, working and networking and, most importantly, re-engineering organisations. The result is a rapid streamlining in operations and management that is fundamentally impossible with paper.

So what of telecommunications? Is a parallel situation evolving? The telephone, the fax machine, mobile phone, television, radio and, more recently, video-conferencing might encourage us to suppose that physical travel will soon be a thing of the past. The reality is that telecommunications is doing for the travel industry what the computer did for the paperless office. We still insist on travelling and meeting people because, the truth is, telecommunications is only a partial solution. In fact telecommunications promote a desire and need to travel for that vital human contact we find so necessary and enjoy. A more recent merging of technology is promoting this world of travel through the combining of computing and communication with laptop computers, modems, fixed line and mobile telephones. We can now be on-line from the car, train, hotel bedroom and we see new age nomads everywhere. They travel with suitcase and laptop, connectors, batteries, modems, mobile phone. For these people the office is where they are; they communicate irrespective of location and distance. Their working style is a far cry from the office worker of just 5 years ago. Indeed, many have no office, and at best, hot desk in a number of locations.

Along with such flexibility and advantage of always being on the move, there is a downside. The divisions between working, playing, home and office are removed. The world becomes a less divided and a far fuzzier place. Work never stops; home life is no longer sacrosanct. But on the upside, those sudden bursts of inspiration and desire to do things can be reconciled immediately. You can work when you are most able, most enthusiastic, best motivated. If managed well it also allows for a great degree of effective human interaction. During the past decade my work output has gone up tenfold through this advance in technology and new mode of working.

The artificial nature of the telephone and teleconferencing will dictate that we continue to travel more than we should, or need, for at least another decade. Beyond that, however, technology will be able to deliver such realism that travel will become anathema. And it is vital that this should be the case, otherwise we stand not only to destroy countries, but the whole of the human environment. Burning hydrocarbons at an accelerating rate is untenable, but burning bits is no problem.

Physicists use the wave theory on Mondays, Wednesdays and Fridays, and the particle theory on Tuesdays, Thursdays and Saturdays.

Sir William
Henry Bragg

Anyone who drives on motorways will have experienced traffic waves created by some unseen event ahead. Probably the best place to experience this phenomenon is on the M25 when, for no apparent reason, the traffic speed can oscillate between 10 and 70mph for long periods. Sometimes the traffic comes to a complete halt and then lurches forward to 40mph and back down to 0. This is the classic behaviour of a system of independent entities in a serial queue having a delay between observation and action. In this case the observation might be an accident, a breakdown, or someone driving foolishly. The delay is between our eye, brain and foot. As soon as we see something and we reach for the brake pedal then very shortly afterwards so does everyone else, and so the wave starts.

There is no doubt about it: rubber necking when driving a car is very dangerous, but people do it. An accident or incident occurs and people slow down to take a look, and then on the far side they speed up. Strangely, when the incident has been cleared away the wave that has been set in motion may last the rest of the day. While the traffic is dense, the wave motion persists long after the event has subsided. The system has an unseen memory – us. Might we then expect similar phenomena in electronic systems for communication between people and machines? This is a racing certainty and the technology and phenomenon is already with us.

Packet switching and transmission systems so beloved of the computer industry are ideal for the creation of information waves. To date these have largely gone unnoticed because terminal equipment assembles packets to construct a complete message, file or picture. The end user sees nothing of the chaotic action inside the network as the information packets jostle for position and queue for transmission. Only when we try to use computer networks for real-time communication do we experience any arrival uncertainties. Our speech sounds strange with varying delays in the middle of utterances and moving pictures contain all manner of distortion and deviation from the truth. The reality is packet systems are fundamentally unsuited to real-time communication between people and machines. So why use them? It turns out that for data communication where arrival time is not an issue, they are highly efficient in their use of bandwidth. These systems were born in an era where bandwidth was expensive and they represent an entirely different paradigm for switching and transmission compared with the telephone network. However, the champions of 'packet everything' always like to tell you that this is the true way for information to be communicated. Curiously they often do this by sending you a single line e-mail message with a 35-line header.

So what of the future? We now have a world of optical fibre and infinite bandwidth, a world of shrinking geography in which distance is becoming irrelevant and in which the fundamental reliability of networks, communication and computing is increasingly dependent upon the electronics used for transmission and switching. If we are to see significant advances in reliability and performance, then the eradication of much of the electronics used today has to be inevitable. The contest will then be between two philosophies, the circuit switching of the telephone network and the path or packet switching of the computer industry. But because an optical fibre is unlike the M25, with a million lanes and no bad drivers, it might just be that these two diverse approaches will coalesce with the switching of light.

telepresence

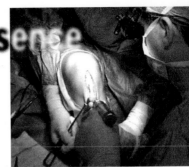

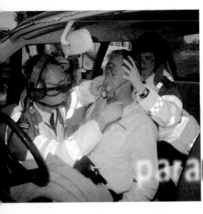

paramedics

stereoscopic

And he that will
this health deny.
Down among the
dead men let
him die.
John Dyer,
1714

Early in the new century the number of people needing some form of daily care and support will more than double, whilst the number of potential carers will fall by a factor of at least 3. At the same time the numbers gainfully employed in creating wealth will halve and those capable of becoming professionals will also fall as a percentage of the total population. Undoubtedly we will also see people failing to provide adequately for an extended old age, and their siblings refusing to pick up the tab. How then are a diminishing band of carers going to cope with a growing customer expectation and demand, when resources and funding will at best remain static, and most likely fall?

No doubt clinicians and carers will continue to refine their techniques and become ever more efficient, whilst administrators shave out costs, reduce bed occupancy, and get patients back into the community ever faster. But none of this will be enough to stem the tide of demand and the growing inability to respond. Something new is required to change the care paradigm that has fundamentally been in stasis for over a century.

At present we see something of a dichotomy as industry delayers and reduces the number of managers, embracing IT and change, whilst healthcare seems to go in the opposite direction. The height of this absurdity has been reached in some American hospitals where each patient now has a dedicated administrator. Also, consider patient records; with the GP, nurse, specialist, consultant, radiologist, anaesthetist gathering the same basic information during just one illness. This is often repeated for successive illnesses and/or visits. The biggest single innovation in patient records during the last century has been to redesign the cart in which the paper is carried.

Patients travel to hospitals; doctors, nurses and specialists travel to patients and hospitals. With head and hand-mounted cameras, VR headsets and video-conferencing, it is now possible to effect remote diagnosis, accident and emergency support of paramedics at an accident site, dermatological examinations, foetal scanning, endoscopy, and operations of all kinds without expensive physical travel.

At a more basic level, consider the nurse who gives up her handbag for a laptop computer, digital camera and GSM mobile phone. At the push of a few keys the abilities of a GP can be extended to some remote location with an image of a wound or infection captured on screen and transmitted back to the remote surgery. Pictorial records of progress can be archived for later comparison and use, whilst reassuring consultancy is always to hand.

Beyond the demands for medical care, we will see a rise in loneliness and need for verbal and visual support. Everyone has TV, radio and telephone, and many have camcorders and PCs. The technology for video-conferencing is now fundamentally inexpensive and available. Support communities on the Internet already exist for just about any disease or condition imaginable. Thousands of people worldwide communicate and compare notes, offering advice and experience beyond that available via traditional routes. Extending this facility to everyone is potentially inexpensive as WWW-TV set-top-box systems roll out at about the price of a SatCom terminal.

Of course there are threats and risks. Smart patients will use IT to get ahead of the professionals. By being better informed they can ask more perceptive questions, demand treatments and be more demanding customers. But worse still, perhaps, countries will export their medical services to compete in other markets. Internet already makes it possible to bypass restrictions on the drugs and medicines available over the counter, and soon it may be diagnosis and treatment that is on immediate offer.

Information networks straddle the world. Nothing remains concealed. But the sheer volume of information dissolves the information. We are unable to take it all in.
Günther Grass, 1990

The medieval librarian was the guardian and regulator of information, the contents list, index, filing system and retrieval mechanism. He alone decided who saw what, when and where. There was no open information access; it was strictly regulated and controlled. So what chance serendipity? Not much. For over 200 years we have enjoyed increasing levels of serendipity with the decimalisation of paper libraries and the librarian's transition from guardian to assistant and information agent. Through this openness we see a high degree of serendipity by merely walking through rows of shelves and chance-spotting that book or obscure journal. Even daily newspapers afford a high degree of serendipity through the mechanisms of headline and picture.

Contrast all of this with the seemingly infinite world of Internet. Here we have almost 100 per cent serendipity; an abundance of data with an overriding lack of order; no sign posts or eye-catching indicators. Actually finding what you want is now a challenge. Being totally awash with serendipity poses a new problem. In this environment, information seems to come in two dominant classes: that which is of no interest, and that which is distracting, interesting, but still of no direct benefit. The problem is now to find anything that you actually require.

Poles apart from Internet, we have the CD-ROM with almost zero serendipity. So well organised, sterile and deep is this medium that drilling down to the information you require can involve over 5 clicks of a mouse. A total lack of visibility of information either side of the mine shaft you dig is also a limiter. You can soon find yourself totally lost and disoriented, with no frame of reference to help – and you resort to Control Quit and start again.

Perhaps somewhere between the Internet and CD-ROM lies the ideal world with the right percentage serendipity that allows us to optimise our creativity and rate of work. The question is, how is it to be realised? Serendipity by design is a major challenge, for in the past we have created such worlds by accident. Perhaps we have to wait for the electronic evolution spontaneously to create this serendipitous environment for us. But I suspect not. For while the world of electronic information is on a scale so colossal it defeats the human mind to contemplate its vastness, we have already experienced the delights of serendipity, and we have some measure of its value to us. Intuitively we feel we should be able to manufacture it.

Perhaps we will have to look to artificial agents who will learn about our habits and interests through direct observation. They would then take on the role of a personal librarian roaming global data banks on our behalf. Perhaps we will have to spend more time with other people discussing our problems and formulating our views to create new forms of serendipity that have so far escaped us. Either way, we face a major challenge as mankind's knowledge base is now doubling in a period of less than 2 years. This is especially so with the creation of increasing levels of short-term information that just act as a fog to us spotting what we are really looking for. We are going to need help through increasing levels of computing power and artificial intelligence. There are no human attributes that will enable us to cope with the massively increased levels of serendipity we now have and will increasingly see. We have to hope that the machines can help us, or face an increasingly sterile and less creative world.

If there is technological advance without social advance, there is, almost automatically, an increase in human misery, in impoverishment.

Michael Harrington, 1962

Quite rightly there is deep concern in many sectors that our society is increasingly becoming divided by the information haves and have-nots. The common perception is that this division is a function of financial wealth. The reality is that the division appears to be strongly weighted by age. Roughly speaking, at 29 years old and above people in the UK are computer illiterate, whilst below this age the chances are they have a degree of computer literacy. Whilst this is a gross generalisation, it does point to a critical division by age and technophobia. Today, our children are born into a world of IT and first encounters with electronic devices are usually in their first year. At the other end of the spectrum we have in our population many who can remember the time before the invention and arrival of the transistor or integrated circuit. They also perceive the technology to be complex, unfriendly and expensive in terms of money and time.

If we are to combat the dangers of an information division in our society, then availability and easy access are vital. Left to its own devices, the industry will probably continue to produce PCs of ever-increasing capability at more or less a constant price. Competition from the brown goods sector may soon change this. The first integrated television and personal computer units have been announced at a price little more than a top end TV. There are also numerous trials on cable and satellite systems using intelligent set-top boxes to provide access to information services and Internet. But perhaps the most exciting future possibility is the development of systems such as Java and low-cost computer terminal and network computing.

Whatever the choice and opportunity provided by technology, by far the biggest hurdle to success is technophobia, and it is age related. The easiest way of breaking down this fear is to get on a machine and succumb to the assistance of an available child. Children come from a world of crash and burn, of experimentation and no handbooks. They consult, confer, and learn very fast. They also delight in helping others, regardless of age. For them the computer screen is a natural place to be, and not a place to be feared.

For those who argue that the disadvantaged are dominated by those facing a financially challenging world, it is interesting to assess the true distribution of wealth. Looking at this problem in terms of the number of television sets, VHS recorders, hi-fi systems and games machines in the average home, along with the money invested in transportation, designer label and luxury clothing, we gain a different picture. It really is a question of how much people value the technology and how useful it is to them that dictates investment patterns and access to the information world. Once people discover the usefulness and powerful nature of this new paradigm, then money is quickly directed into purchasing equipment and software.

One challenge that hits rich and poor in this IT world is to keep up to date, for within 3 years a top end product will become outmoded and start to look lame. However, that does not preclude their use in education and training in the broad sense. It does not make them totally useless, just limited.

Then, of course, there is the issue of the cost of communication and connection. When it comes to getting on-line and cruising the Internet, it is interesting to compare the cost to that of purchasing or hiring videos, running a car, a pint of beer or the purchase of a very few other luxury goods. None of this technology is really all that expensive.

In just over 2,000,000 years we have become *numero uno* in the intelligence stakes, but our wetware looks to have reached its evolutionary peak. Weighing in at around 1kg, the human brain is about 10cm in diameter, contains some 10,000,000,000 neurons, and a connectivity of around 10,000 per neuron. In our recent past Neanderthal man had a brain 15–20 per cent larger and the potential to be smarter. But a number of key factors appear to have precluded this possibility. First, the inability to remove heat without the cooling (vascular) systems dominating the brain space – we generate about the same heat output as a 50W lightbulb in a 10cm cavity. Second, the signal transmission span and synaptic speed is dictated by reaction times essential to avoid physical threats and danger. There are also limiting trade-offs between the size of the vascular system and the density, capacity and synaptic interconnection. Intelligence depends on rapid and massive signal processing of pulses at the synapses. In computer terms the pulse width is linked to the clock speed, and processing cannot occur faster than a single clock cycle. If pulses cannot be made shorter then they dictate the maximum processing speed.

For our metabolism to support a bigger brain would mean more blood flow, faster food-to-energy conversion, and a stronger neck. A much larger brain would need more damping for shock absorption when accelerating and decelerating. With a 1m diameter head we would be in danger of suffering concussion every time we started or stopped walking as our brain crashed into the inside of our skull.

When the combination of processing time at synapses, transmission speed along axons, and neural density are considered, then the connectivity we now enjoy appears near optimal for processing performance. However, as a model, it does not appear to be a definitive guide for designing other systems, a prerequisite of an intelligent system, or an overall limit. Whales and dolphins have larger brains, but with large portions specialised to SONAR processing and communication over long distances. They also enjoy a larger vascular system and heat-benign environment.

While the measurable difference in size, and perhaps structure, of male and female has become a high point of political correctness, it may have a basis in purpose and role. Size/intelligence estimates show little difference and may even favour the smaller brain as having a marginally better packing density and connectivity. But this difference looks to be related to the need to throw projectiles accurately with thousands of our neurons acting in parallel to overcome their individual noisy nature. Unlike silicon brains, ours deal in uncertainty, with the biological neurons constructed from about 1000 individual cells. Such a small number of base elements makes them essentially noisy – in some respects, quantum devices. In stark contrast we design transistorised logic to switch with great precision. One world is full of life, emotion and intelligence; the other is cold, deterministic and dead. This realisation has recently seen the engineering of noisy neural networks purposely arranged not to be deterministic.

So what separates us and our noisy neurons from those in the latest machines? Only scale and sensors. Our awareness comes from sight, sound, touch, smell and taste. We can now give all of this to a machine in a form that could be superior to ours. They could have experience over a far wider spectrum than we, and also have additional abilities. It would thus seem that the only limiter is scale. Given the present rate of progress, the year 2015 may see us equalled. What price political correctness when we have man, woman and machine? It might just be that machine born of man will be smartest of all.

M15 ARE ALL BITS REALLY EQUAL?

All animals are equal but some animals are more equal than others.

George Orwell, 1945

It's not unusual to hear pundits declare that a bit is a bit is a bit. The philosophically held belief is that 'all bits are made equal in the eyes of man and machine.' Well, even the Romans (Petronius Arbiter *c*. 60AD) figured out that the most important message was the least expected one, and thus all bits are not equal. So, is a telephone bit really the same value as a TV bit? Sometimes this is undoubtedly the case, but a fire alarm or burglar alarm bit really is worth knowing about. And the bit that says your pacemaker is about to fail has even more value. We also require that the validity and security of a TV bit be a vastly different proposition from a bank account or aircraft control system bit. Whatever machines may do or think, it is clear that all bits are not of equal importance or value in the eyes of mankind.

Looking to the telephone network and the Internet we generally see no costing or classification of bits by worth. From a transport perspective all bits and messages are treated the same. Historically, telephone bits have been seen as expensive, and to date remain dominated by distance, speed and hold-time related charges. However, the trend is towards reducing infrastructure costs and a decoupling of cost and distance travelled. On the net the illusion has been that bits are free, which they are not – someone has to pay. The rise of pay per click advertising, commercial services and bit prioritisation between real and delayed time applications will rapidly kill the illusion of total freedom and bit equality.

In a parallel universe of bit delivery, cable, satellite and terrestrial TV networks totally ignore distance and supply everything in real time. The considerable expense of doing this is funded by advertising and over delivery of huge quantities of junk bits. However, the principal money earners are the emotional bits. This is the emotion conveyed by chat shows, news, sport and blockbuster movies. It also includes the emotional engagement and demand of the viewers who feel they must witness that sporting event right now. If pay per view is emotionally driven, then perhaps this is also true of the allocation of advertising revenues and licence fees that support terrestrial TV. Viewer ratings are emotionally driven. Why else do people watch the programmes? Of course it could be plain habit or addiction, but either way any assumption that all bits are equal seems tenuous.

In an interactive world of multimedia the opportunity to charge by bit type, distance, speed and usage is with us, but extremely difficult to tap. In today's telephone networks billing operations are becoming huge and unwieldy, consuming vast resources, and tending towards the uneconomic. The same is true of satellite and cable operations that venture far beyond rental and simple encryption card purchase. In the information world the problem may become really acute as the number of vendors potentially includes all of us – we can be both consumers and suppliers.

In macro-economies based on micro-prices, you cannot pay 20p, 2p or 0.2p for individual items with a cheque or a credit card. The processing costs of billing for the exchange of goods for such small amounts of money swamp the per item cost. It is already clear that some businesses can no longer collect their charges economically, and as costs fall further, they could go out of business. So it might just be that in a commerce of bits the complexity of differentiating between bits and collecting the money might, by default, ultimately render all bits equal.

Information is the oxygen of the modern age. It seeps through the walls topped by barbed wire, it wafts across the electrified borders.

Ronald Reagan, 1989

My early career was dominated by paper, usually in triplicate, with processing times between groups stretching out to 12 or more days. Drafting a letter, having it typed, corrected and signed off could take 2 or 3 days. Internal and external mail systems would add another 2 days, or more. A letter drafted on a Monday morning would be posted late on Friday, arrive the following Monday, and then the process began again in reverse. Often, a single copy of the correspondence was circulated to several people before a reply was written, with each person adding to the processing time. So all in all, a 12-day turnaround was seen as very respectable.

Today such delays are intolerable, and the use of fax, telephone and e-mail have drastically reduced the amount of surface mail, as processes speed up. Typing pools and many secretaries have disappeared as more managers become IT literate. So it is worth asking: what is the ultimate response time?

I live in a 100 per cent electronic environment induced by returning or destroying all internally generated snail mail that could have been sent electronically. But I also promise to respond to all electronic communications within 12 hours. This is a 24-hour a day 365-day of the year obligation on my part. To date my average response time to any e-mail message is 3 hours with 99 per cent answered within 12 hours. So what about the 1 per cent? It is inevitable that during some periods of travel on long international flights, or for reasons of family commitments, the 12-hour rule is occasionally violated.

Until recently I faced a real challenge – the lack of sockets. No phone, hotel room or office was safe; I was always hunting for sockets. As soon as I entered a building, I would plug in, log on, drop my processed mail, then pick up the next batch. While on the face of it this might seem an easy oper- ation, and one that would not cause a technologist too much difficulty, the number of different types of socket, sys- tem delays and other variables that induce pain are almost infinite. For example, the same RG11 telephone connector is used in Europe and the USA, but unfortunately the wires are inconveniently shifted over by one pin. So very often you can't just plug in. Even now I go everywhere armed with screwdrivers, crocodile clips and a selection of connec- tors. This inconvenience is compounded by an incredible variety of dial tones, digital and analogue transmission sys- tems, that introduce a variety of signal echoes and distor- tion. Even a hotel room with 3 telephones can cause significant difficulties, especially if you don't spot the tele- phone in the toilet that may have to be unplugged.

But now there is GSM – digital mobile telephony. What an advance. Now I can live a near socket-free life, on-line from car, train, hotel and restaurant. I can roam across Europe without worry (apart from France, of course, where the dial codes have to be different) and always be on-line. If only they had GSM in North America. Unfortunately the system standards and coverage of TDMA in Europe and CDMA in North America are totally different. There is also a lack of 100 per cent geographical coverage, so total mobility is not quite possible. Those long Atlantic flights also contribute to my 1 per cent failure – although there is a shaver point in the toilet, there is no phone socket. But as I travel 150,000 miles a year, you may be able to do better than I. For my foreseeable future it looks as though the socket hunt will continue. So save a place for screwdrivers and crocodile clips.

A man must rise above the earth to the top of the atmosphere and beyond, for only then will he fully understand the world in which he lives.

Socrates, c.399 BC.

Managing a modern company can be like flying an airliner with more instrumentation than is actually necessary. You can see the temperature of the coffee cups but your altitude and heading is anybody's guess. You are data rich and information poor, and VR has a big, and largely unrecognised, part to play. It is ideally suited to the representation of highly complex and data-rich situations. Visualising the operational information of a company is far more edifying than a spreadsheet.

We are very pictographic animals, able to absorb animated, 3D colour images at a phenomenal rate. It is unnatural for us to read and write, or interpret spreadsheets; we are soon overloaded by information in such formats. Moreover, many of our species have a natural ability mentally to translate 2D drawings (plans) into a 3D world (models). And yet, if information is presented in a natural 3D form, we are all inherently able to absorb and understand the equivalent of a 20-volume encyclopedia in about 15 seconds.

Designing all but the simplest modern products and artefacts on paper has now had its day. Moving to VR affords greater clarity and understanding, facilitates simulation and testing, and as a result, great savings. The need to drastically shorten time to market, and get products right first time, has brought this technology to the fore. Producing anything from a mobile phone through to an airline passenger terminal can see savings of over 30 per cent in time and money through the use of VR. Visualising the final design in full (virtual) operation is a vital step in getting it right, but without the expense of an actual build.

Medical applications are developing rapidly with everything from body fly-throughs to operation simulations and

augmented reality

immersion

visualisation

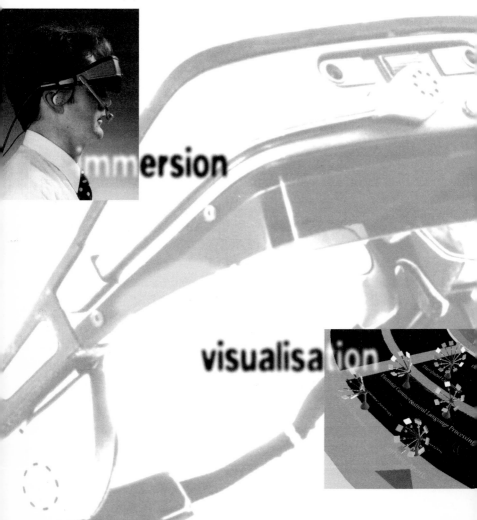

animations. In this area, along with many others, it is the mixing of the real and virtual worlds where the greatest advantage probably lies. Combining telepresence and VR allows surgeons the benefit of a real world view augmented by computer-generated simulations. In recent trials surgeons have been able to stand 'one inside the other' at a distance to experience new surgical techniques for the first time, or receive reassurance during a first-time solo operation. This technology is equally applicable to the repair of a computer, oil refinery, jet engine or heating plant. It offers a new and alternative approach to education – a metaphoric guide on the inside.

VR also offers significant potential for the teaching of science, mathematics and many other topics. It is principally a medium for direct experience and we can now step inside the atom or molecule, fly a proton and experience fission, rather than just gaze at a set of complex equations. We can also dissect a virtual frog and operate a virtual microscope. For the first time we can see and feel the binding energies in the alignment process of a long chain molecule while simultaneously viewing the equations and associated graphical information. For many well-understood systems we can already view and handle mathematical functions and models in a new way. They no longer have to be artificially frozen in time and space by the limitation of paper, but can be alive with N-dimensional interactivity.

It is interesting to reflect that only 50 years ago classes at schools and universities were commonly augmented by practical demonstrations on a laboratory bench that may still be in the front row today. Effectively that was VR 50 years ago – you just sat and watched someone else do it. Today much more can be done on the screen by everyone. It may be the tool we have been looking for – instant education and understanding – just in time.

The unpredictability inherent in human affairs is due largely to the fact that the by-products of a human process are more fateful than the product.

Eric Hoffer, 1973

Because telephone customers make only a few short duration calls at random times each day, they require access to only a small fraction of the total switching and network fabric. A residential line might typically see 3 calls of 3 minutes per day, made at more or less random times, whilst business lines may be over 20 of slightly longer duration. The resource sharing increases beyond the local switch, as traffic is concentrated into a hierarchical global network, and only in the local loop do we all need a dedicated connection. This analysis was characterised by A.K. Erlang, a Danish telephone pioneer working around 1917, and has become holy writ, involving negative exponential distributions and queuing theory. Simply put: as the number of users grows, then the more resource aggregation is possible, and the longer you are on the phone, the more likely you are to terminate. Historically, two-hour calls are rare.

Some years ago, a discussion with a computer network team brought home to me just how much the telephone network might have to change. Computer users had complained about the lack of bandwidth and latency, while measurements had established the LAN (Local Area Network) loading to be 25 per cent. After some probing, this figure turned out to be the average over a full day. It was then discovered that the average loading for 1-hour periods could exceed 55 per cent; whilst 10-minute periods returned 95 per cent. The real shock came when the 1-minute figure revealed loadings in excess of 300 per cent. Here was the problem, a now-obvious oversight: a massive peak to mean ratio never experienced in telephone networks.

This problem has since become much worse with the emergence of the Internet. Highly correlated network activities have seen the peak to mean ratio increase rapidly to create the World Wide Wait. Whilst the bit transport problem can be solved by providing more bandwidth, a more holistic approach might be to examine network protocols and topologies. We might then simultaneously relieve the strain on routers, switches and servers.

A growing problem for telephone networks is the hold times associated with net access from fixed and mobile terminals. Instead of 3 minutes, the average can now be hours, or in the case of polling systems, less than a minute. The Erlang model fails under these extremes because the underlying assumptions are wrong, and resource sharing on a grand scale breaks down.

Large numbers of people making very long telephone calls to a local server rapidly clog up the switching fabric for normal users. This also results in the balance of local and long-distance calls being distorted, which necessitates a different network investment profile. On a personal level, users find they cannot make calls, and miss calls when they are on-line longer than they think. The solution? Well, it appears that most of us just have to get a second phone line.

For those systems polling regularly with very short hold times designed to minimise connection costs, it is even worse. Telephone signalling, control and billing systems were never designed for such a high rate of set-up and clear-down. So access can also be blocked by CPU overload.

But this is only the start. Network computing, and TV access to the net through set-top boxes, will introduce new on-line activities that could swell the population of users very fast. They will be totally reliant upon the telephone network for all applications and services. The problem will be the lack of sharing, and it looks like we need a new Mr Erlang – and a new network model.

Man is still
the most
extraordinary
computer of all.
John F. Kennedy,
1963

In an increasingly digital world, being a predominantly analogue entity is getting tougher. Faster digital machines present a significant mismatch to us and our bio-systems. At best we can estimate we take in about 1Gbit/s visually, but require about 7Gbit/s for full head and eye tracking; and a full spatial model requires some 900Gbit/s. Non-intrusive scanning mechanisms show this form of information as a reasonably localised flush of energy consumption or neural activity in our brain. The same is true of acoustic, tactile, taste and smell stimulation, but to a much smaller degree.

At a conservative estimate, and assuming we could use every corner of our brain, which we cannot, each of us could store about 5000 years'-worth of continuous conversation, and about 5 years'-worth of continuous video. Well, on one plane, thank God we are analogue and do forget. Our analogue memory system seems to have evolved to let information fade exponentially, and perhaps to imagine it could do otherwise is the stuff of dreams. The problem is that we have new IT-driven demands bringing a need to remember and process increasingly more as we communicate, work, travel and meet more people.

I have long considered computers to be my third lobe. They are the place where I store and process everything with greater precision than nature would normally allow with my carbon-based wetware. Looking to the future, can these two worlds of analogue and digital forms coexist symbiotically? Could we really communicate directly with machines? Well, perhaps not for a while it would seem, but all the indications are promising.

There have now been over 1700 successful cochlea implants, involving chips mounted inside the human head, to restore the hearing of those suffering severe hearing difficulties. From an engineering perspective you might suppose that connecting the correct carbon-based nerves into the correct silicon feeds would be a major problem. But it seems not to be so. The wife of a friend has been profoundly deaf for over 50 years and recently had cochlea implants. Being a smart lady she set about tutoring her brain by using a talking book in conjunction with the printed page. Playing the talking book into her electronic ears while reading the same words saw her having her first stilted conversations within weeks. After a couple of years she has become remarkably proficient, and is not on her own; thousands are now emulating this process. Of course, what they hear might not be as good as the real thing, but it works, it is a beginning and our technology is, as yet, very crude.

Similar experiences are also recorded with prosthetics coupled directly into the human nervous system. Furthermore, there are serious attempts at nervous system repair with silicon bypass, and there has been just one experiment with an artificial retina. The precise wiring diagram does not seem to matter; we no longer seem to have to obey the engineers' cable colour code. While our electronics is immutable in its configuration, the human system seems able to reprogram the I/O to accommodate this limitation. What a miracle. Our very adaptable and analogue nature seems to be able to accommodate our engineering system limitations.

It is interesting that recent developments in optical storage and processing technology are seeing a swing back to analogue forms that are more efficient than digital electronics. We should reflect that our biological systems are actually an interesting mix of analogue and digital. Might this be where our true synergy lies – where carbon meets silicon – where the dominantly digital meets the dominantly analogue – where mind meets machine?

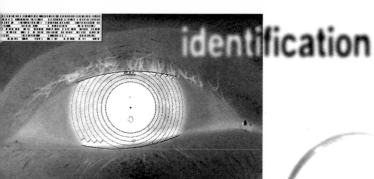

identification

scan

recognition

He that has eyes to see and ears to hear may convince himself that no mortal can keep a secret. If his lips are silent, he chatters with his fingertips; betrayal oozes out of him at every pore.
Sigmund Freud, 1905

The very idea of making a purchase by giving someone your charge card or bank account details over the telephone, or worse, Internet, fills many people with fear. They see it as risky and very insecure. But these same people buy petrol, food and goods from stores, and are very happy to hand over their card so a copy can be made, complete with a legible signature. In doing so they never question or worry about the honesty of the recipient of this prized and protected information.

I was recently challenged by a man who claimed that his digital mobile phone was 100 per cent secure. This I refuted. When asked to divulge the secret of how I would listen into his conversation, I replied with the simplest of eavesdropping techniques – I would just sit at the side of him. People on mobile phones are seldom guarded in what they say as they assume themselves to be in some kind of acoustic bubble. So electronic crime does not always need fancy technology, just opportunism.

There is no such thing as security. It is a dream. Security is not an absolute quantity, only a relative commodity. The reality is that most security failures are down to human fallibility: bribery, and corruption. Granted, electronic break-ins are on the increase, but so is the theft of entire machines. And how is this so different from the world of paper? Well, only in its scale and apparent invisibility.

In contrast to modern technology, entire legal systems stand or fall by pen and ink; the human signature is legally binding and held as proof. It is also one of the easiest things to forge. Paper money, gold and silver are easy to steal, but require physical action that is visible. Electronic crime, on the other hand, can introduce new dimensions of reach, scale and anonymity.

So what of cryptography? Surely that is really secure? Well, not necessarily. No matter how long the key sequence or coding process, future computers (of exponentially greater power than today) will be able to search all the combinations in a reasonably short time. For example, a modest home computer can search all the combinations in a 40-bit sequence in a week or so. With a main frame this falls to a few seconds. More impressively, cracking codes lends itself to parallelism. So all we have to do is link tens of Power PCs to realise a tremendous capability. No matter how long the sequence or code used, the computer to crack it will arrive sooner or later.

Of course, we can reduce the odds against electronic crime by changing code sequences on each operation, but this can be expensive and inconvenient. So, I would put my money on the concatenation of several codes or simple overt and covert protection devices. If we spend thousands of pounds it is possible to recognise a face, voice, hand, fingerprint, and other biometrics with a billions to one chance of an error. However, for just a few hundred pounds we can realise error probabilities around one in a thousand. Applying four or five of these techniques in succession can rapidly achieve error probabilities in the hundreds of billions to one. Super-security can therefore be both low cost and convenient.

Now, back to the original problem. When we wish to spend money, the vendor wants to know it is us, and that we have the money to spend. We, on the other hand, should be gauging the honesty of the vendor and the security of the transaction. Ultimately the weak link is the people involved, and it may be some time before machines can outsmart or catch us.

M21 JUST PICTURE IT

What is the use of a book without pictures or conversations?

Alice in Wonderland, Lewis Carroll

An old Chinese proverb attributed to Confucius (*c*.500 BC) states: 'I hear and I forget; I see and I remember; I do and I understand.' Several thousand years ago this was profoundly insightful. The implications of such thinking ought to be even more obvious today. But when you look at our democracy, bureaucracy and institutions, you could be convinced we had learned nothing. Even Internet is dominated by an infinity of words. What is this burdensome focus on text?

The world's libraries now store well over 100 million original volumes. So, in one sense, it is now easier to write the book you want rather than try to find it. But resting on these shelves are the Lord's Prayer (*c*. 70 words), the 23rd Psalm (115 words), and the Ten Commandments (135 words). These are the basic tenets by which a large percentage of the human race live. In contrast, the documentation defining the pricing of cabbages in the EEC consumes nearly 7000 words. This is almost 5 times as many as those used in the Declaration of Independence for the United States (1488 words). Why do we use unnecessary prose to describe everyday situations and objects? Have we lost the ability to be concise? Apart from wearing out our eyes, the sheer human effort needed to generate the mountains of words, the confusion they cause, and the storage space they demand, beggars belief. Why not keep it simple, and use fewer words and more pictures?

Perhaps our processes of communication are becoming like the fast food industry, confused by the richness of options and the efficacy of quality and quantity. In the extreme we have press, radio and TV highly dependent on the snapshot, sound and/or video bite. Seldom are we given the opportunity to judge on the basis of the full story. So very often it seems that really important issues hit the page and screen for the briefest of periods, while reams of paper and air time are devoted to the trivial and insignificant. Until recently we have not had the network mechanisms to allow us our own, individual, in-depth analysis, but IT might ultimately provide the solution.

I have often pondered the strange phenomenon of the on-line newspaper with the printed page reproduced directly on the screen verbatim. As far as I can see, no account has been taken of the change in medium – from printed page to network and PC. To ignore the ability to combine text and pictures with audio and video, let alone interaction, seems about as sensible as double-entry book-keeping on a PC. By and large, a direct transfer from paper to screen is always a bad move.

When I was at school and college I attended classes on communication and creative writing. Perhaps we now need courses on creative communication which involve the simultaneous exploitation of all the variables offered by our developing technology. I cannot imagine that Shakespeare, Browning or Dickens would have restricted themselves to quill, parchment and paper, if the multimedia choices we enjoy today had been available to them. My guess is they would have recorded their plays, verse and stories using technology to the full. The world would not have been left to interpret exactly what they meant; all would have been much clearer and richer. Come to think of it, so might the law, the legislation of governments and operational documents of companies and institutions.

When we travelled less and telephones were all on the end of a wire, you could be reasonably sure of making direct contact with people. Today our world has become more complex. In less than 8 years over 10 per cent of all telephones have become mobile, with ever more fax and answering machines. How many times do you call someone to find they are out, indisposed, or have apparently been replaced by a machine? Telephone tag is becoming an international sport.

In the days of lesser mobility there was a 98 per cent chance someone would be at their place of work, and a 90 per cent chance that they would be at the side of their fixed telephone. Call and rental charges were much higher then and calls shorter and fewer. So there was only about a 10 per cent chance that you would receive engaged tone, no reply or non-availability. For over 80 per cent of the working day you could contact the person of your choice, and in most cases someone would answer the phone, talk to you and take a message. How different today.

Many people now travel so much that they occupy their office for only about 70 per cent of the time, and business intensity sees them in conversation, meetings and otherwise indisposed for 70 per cent of the day. So we have a slice of the working population available to answer the telephone for only about 50 per cent of the time. But there are more calls of longer duration, and a contact window of less than 35 per cent is not uncommon. So if we do not get busy tone, then for at least 65 per cent of the time a machine answers, or we are diverted to a series of unanswered extensions, ultimately to be ignored or answered by an unknowing human who takes a message.

Resorting to a mobile phone generally sees a marginal

improvement, with users switched on for over 80 per cent of the time. But there is still a 30 per cent chance of them being indisposed to the point of non-reply. So, for about 50 per cent of the time call diversion or answering machines deal with the rest. In general the contact window hovers just above 50 per cent.

In part, this has all contributed to the growing popularity of voice mail, messaging and e-mail for fixed and mobile working. They all put delay back into the communication process where it is required. This helps to relieve those suffering acute information overload – exacerbated by continual electronic interruptions. These relatively new modes of communication do not suffer from the distracting immediacy of the fixed and mobile telephone. For many people we seem to have reached a point of needing to find a means of managing communication and information flow to restore a reasonable balance in the whole process. The limits to human communication, information I/O and processing are now the fundamental limit to our activities. We are the weak link in the chain of progress.

A further debilitating problem beyond our limited ability to access, process and I/O data, is our inability to network. Even the Romans were aware of the problem and organised legions by tens or thereabouts. Modern companies and organisations often rediscover this fundamental limit to the span of human communication and control. In contrast, machines do not suffer from such limitations and can extend our abilities to thousands of people. But for us this means broadcast rather than dialogue. Within the next decade we are going to have to reassess the way in which we choose to talk to each other and machines. But the priority is to get something intelligent to answer when we call.

M23 MATHEMATICS AND BIGGER BRAINS

Mathematics is the door and key to the sciences.
Roger Bacon, 1267

As a student I was besotted by the power of mathematics and physical modelling. My enthusiasm was fuelled by the fact that, barring a few generalising assumptions and simplifications of real-world situations, most of the problems I was presented with could be solved by one technique or another. For me the power of the mathematical process, the training, clear thinking and ability it invokes cannot be understated, and is in stark contrast to the less quantifiable sciences and humanities.

Like everyone else I was in an education system that lulled me into a false sense of security, as I was fed a continual diet of problems that had solutions. This convinced me that our universe was largely well behaved, with a few non-linear areas that were difficult, but could mostly be avoided. When I moved into industry it came as a shock to find the converse was true. We can solve almost nothing – relatively speaking. Our universe is principally non-linear, and we get by mostly with approximations to reality, or even gross misrepresentations. I am still surprised that we have been able to engineer and achieve as much as we have given the oft crudeness of our models and understanding of reality.

Reflecting upon this recently, I pondered the way we teach mathematics. Given the critical dependence of our civilisation on the subject, it seems paradoxical that it lacks any general acclaim or popularity. For most people it usually invokes a dull ache, fear and mysticism. Perhaps this is because the process of acquiring mathematical skills is generally protracted and painful. While it is often perceived as a nightmare topic, the truth is, with good teaching most people can become reasonably competent. However, the time and effort needed to acquire even a modest capability can be excessive by today's standards.

When ancient man first attached a sharp stone to a stick to create a spear, he did not seek out a target and then apply a mathematical formula for the force and trajectory. He got by with trial and error, eventually leading to some exceptional encephalisation of his brain over millennia. Not until Newton arrived did the physical and mathematical detail get attended too in a rigorous manner. To this day we still teach our students from formula towards action and projectile. Worse, we divorce them from the physical reality through computers producing numbers to such accuracy as to obscure the uncertainties of the physical process.

Performing real experiments and making observations prior to mathematical modelling, measuring the outcome of trials against predictions, is powerful stuff. But combining this with on-screen modelling introduces a further level of clarity and dimension for understanding. Plotting a trajectory is only the first stage; introducing the influence of air turbulence and throwing action variations adds much more depth of understanding and insight to the complexity involved.

Highly complex systems such as airflow over an aircraft wing, gas flow in a turbine, fluid motion and neural networks, defy mathematical analysis for all but the most stable situations. Non-linearity and chaos dominate the real world and may always fall outside our established routes to solution and understanding. But it is in this realm that we are likely to make the most exciting discoveries and advances. What we require is that intuitive feel for what the final outcome is likely to be, and the sensitivities of the processes to input changes. Perhaps the computer can be our stone on a stick, the means by which we move on to understand. Only this time, it will be computers that enjoy the encephalisation, not us.

We have a layer of clay that prevents anything moving either way – up or down. The layer is middle management.

Heini Lippuner, Ciba CEO, 1991

Traditionally, most organisations have been strictly hierarchical and based upon the power and control of individuals or individual groups. Steep pyramids of power and laws have been the name of the game for centuries. However, technological change is now challenging this established and well-tried model. It is effectively shaking out the need for the many layers of management dictated by old technologies and wisdoms.

When the US army invaded Granada a single GI came under fire from 10 policemen. Being outnumbered, he called HQ by radio and asked what he was to do. The reply was a singular order – shoot them. It later transpired that this order was given by a four-star general in person. So the question arose: what are all the intervening ranks for, and what were they doing?

Desert Storm saw the US troops without an approved personal Navistar system. So back home mom and pop went to Radio Shack and bought $300 GPS units and mailed them direct to their sons in the featureless desert. It also turned out that the most reliable piece of IT was a laser jet printer purchased from a high-street store. So the question arose: why bother with military specification and procurement?

These examples reflect technologies that induce fundamental operational and organisational change. No wonder companies are downsizing and delayering. Improved communication and computing allow the old-style management chains and processes to be bypassed. Companies that had five layers of management can now get by with only two, and as a result they become more dynamic and responsive. It is as if the intermediate layers were in place to stop organisations becoming successful. If true, it is not by design, more by culture and tradition. Managers who act as information and control intermediaries create unnecessary delays and inaction. Holding onto information, people and control, used to be a way of maintaining position and staying employed. Today it is the kiss of death for the individual and the company.

So why do modern armies still have all those ranks when commanders have direct radio access to all their troops? Well, it appears to be a combination of mindset, tradition, and the fear and risk of change. No one, apart from a despot, wants to gamble with human lives. But this is not a problem if all the armies in the world maintain the status quo. It is only a problem if one army makes a successful change and becomes a far more effective and superior machine. In modern business there is no status quo; many have moved, or are on the move, and competition leaves us with no choice. We have to become more efficient and responsive. Management delayering and outsourcing on an increased scale is inevitable if we are to keep markets and maintain low costs.

The really successful and fast developing companies are now more like amorphous blobs than hierarchical armies of ranked officers. Although production lines and processes still demand the stability of structure, increased levels of automation put even this under threat. So we can expect more pressure from the ever-shortening lifetimes of products and industries, with most of us facing more change than all previous generations.

It should be recognised that none of this can be realised by blindly cutting out people. Without a considered and co-ordinated investment in technology, new working practices, processes, and most importantly of all, people education and training, it can all go badly wrong. To tackle one or two, and not all, facets of change, can be fatal. But getting it right can mean survival and a very healthy bottom line.

60

With affection beaming in one eye, and calculation shining out of the other.

Charles Dickens, Mrs Todgers in Martin Chuzzlewit

Ever since the invention of television we seem to have had a fixation for a windows mode of viewing. Whilst reasonably adequate for entertainment, it is severely limiting for IT, and especially portable devices. The arrival of the liquid crystal display has made the limitations even more obvious. With a contrast ratio and brightness a fraction of the cathode ray tube; severe washout in bright sunlight; poor or zero operation at low temperatures; slow response times and numerous optical artefacts, they are far from ideal. Perhaps it's time for a change, time for a new technology.

Why do we take a beam of electrons and illuminate a panel that we then view at a distance? Why not take a beam of photons and inject it direct into the eye to create a pure image on our retina? All the intermediate stages of conversion from electron bombardment, to phosphor excitation and photon generation, only serve to detract from the efficiency and final quality. Why do it that way when it is possible to take over the entire visual cortex and create a real sense of being somewhere else – real or artificial?

It is now reasonable to suppose that a laser-based projection system could be mounted on a contact lens or spectacle frame. However, it turns out that this dream of an active contact lens is beyond today's technology. The power supply currently presents problems, and the circuit lithography (printing) required is just not fine enough – yet. But a head-mounted device is feasible. We therefore have in prospect new windows into information worlds without the burden of large boxes of technology.

Along with computers that talk to us, we might now perceive a world where they share our visual field in much the same way that 'The Terminator' was able simultaneously to

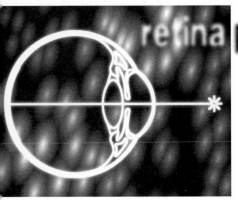

retina projection

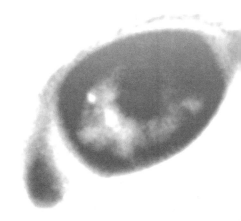

contact lens

bodyworn

view real world images and digital readouts. As a species we have an amazing ability to multi-task – reading a newspaper while listening to the radio is perhaps one of the most common occurrences. In contrast, television demands our attention and is an ideal instrument of distraction. Curiously it would appear that we have an innate ability to live in more than one world at once through multiple visual and acoustic inputs. Information from the real world can enter one eye and one ear while at the same time information from computer-generated worlds can take over the remaining organs.

Now we come to the thorny problem of protocol, convention and what is acceptable. We are extremely perceptive and very conscious of facial expression and eye contact. When I look at you and I see an animated graph, my favourite TV programme, or a page of text hovering in free space above your head, will we still be able to communicate? This might be tricky if the data is your CV, medical record, or a briefing on your company and your activities.

The smallest mobile telephone now weighs only 100 grams and our world hovers on a move away from the PC in the direction of network computing. And there is a growing enthusiasm and interest in body-worn computers and communicators. Put all these together with a head-mounted projector, constructed from lasers the size of a salt crystal, and we have in prospect a very different world. But it doesn't stop there, for along with micro-miniature projectors come micro-miniature cameras and the possibility of shared worlds. At that point what I see, you see, what I read, you read and vice versa.

Our memories are card indexes consulted and then returned in disorder by authorities whom we do not control.
Cyril Connolly, 1944

Somewhere in your deepest memory is probably a scene at the seaside with parents and family when you were 10 or so years old. If you think about that day it will be recalled in reasonably vivid detail you might consider to be fact. But should you have a photograph from the day, the difference between reality and recollection will be very significant. Why is this? Well, we are more analogue than digital and our memory process is Hebbian. That is, reinforcement is followed by exponential decay with time. So unless we regularly refresh our memory, events and remembrances start to part company.

In stark contrast, machines are dominantly digital and therefore record everything with precision and longevity. Couple this with the human tendency to record everything and throw nothing away and we are faced with mountains of worthless data. We are often data rich and information poor. In the paper world of the past many of us instituted regimes of yearly culls of filing cabinets. Files would be taken out and reduced to a tenth of their thickness by mercilessly dispatching huge amounts of paper to the shredding machine. That regime has now been reborn in the cyclic culling of information on PCs and mainframes. But it has got much worse, with multiple copies and versions on multiple machines in multiple locations. How do we cope? I don't think we can. Trying to operate two PCs in two locations, and keep them synchronised, seems impossible. Add a laptop, and the level of difficulty seems to accelerate away from us. So what to do?

Although machines are digital, it is not beyond us to introduce Hebbian mechanics to exponentially cull information triggered by its lack of usage. In many organisations information now has a half-life of 6 months or less. And yet we still record and store it as if it was of value, which it is not. As a first step in this direction software can check on the last access date of information, and after a predetermined time, remove all colour, logos and non-essential information. Later, automatic summarising can cut documents down to their very essence. Progressively doing this sees documents in a fit state to be destroyed, or merely left as a headstone in some remote and little-used memory space.

Such systems are not difficult to engineer and do work, but I have to confess to also destroying vast amounts of information and never filing it in the first place. People often seem to confuse communication, quality and quantity, and certainly when dealing with some institutions it is often better to bin rather than even attempting to read and file.

In another corner of my life I have experimented with a novel way of filing. This I call uni-heap. Because I come from a world of paper I have been conditioned to putting electronic information in folders and neatly storing it on my hard disc. Indeed this is a very useful and powerful mechanism for creating order, stability and efficiency. However, in the world of e-mail that comes thick and fast, there is no time to file, no time to sort, and merely throwing all the messages into a big pile seems sufficient. The search and find capability of a PC brings to the fore all messages on any topic or from any group or person almost instantly and then it can just be thrown back on the heap. I suspect my mind works like this too. If only I could get it to cull all the irrelevant and never-used items – I might have enough capacity for the rest of my life.

The chief reason warfare is still with us is...the simple fact that no substitute for this final arbiter in international affairs has yet appeared on the political scene. Hannah Arendt, 1972

By and large young people have an affinity for IT through early exposure and fearless experimentation. They prefer not to read handbooks or ask questions, but to just do it. Most parents and older people do not share this mindset as they come from a different world lacking exposure and experience.

Even as a technologist, multi-function buttons and other interface twists sometimes give me grief. It took me a while to discover that ejecting an audio cassette from my car radio meant depressing the play button for four seconds. Not obvious to me, but it was for my young son. In this case the ability divide was not one of technophile and technophobe, it was just a mindset difference. As a general rule such fractures between generations are age related through experience and expectation – a bit like acquiring a bad golf swing.

For the very young, the process of learning to interface with technology is done by raw experimentation, trial and error. You get on a machine and you fly until you crash, and then you reset and start again. This is repeated until you become proficient. As a process it is incremental and handbook free, like learning to walk and run. Whilst older generations might view playing computer games as a waste of time, they are a sure way of overcoming technophobia and acquiring essential skills.

There is no doubt that IT has a great potential to create couch potatoes and unthinking people, but on the other hand it also is a great enabler and means of educating faster than ever before. Children are like sponges for information, experience and understanding. With IT they can go at their own pace and feel unabashed at experimenting. They are never intimidated by mere technology, only people. In some studies it has been found that youngsters can absorb information 50 per cent faster and retain 80 per cent more in the pictographic and interactive world of multimedia. In some cases it is even greater; in others, far less. The advantage is strongly linked to the topic – unfortunately we do not seem to have discovered a means of burning the multiplication tables or spelling and grammar into the human brain other than by rote.

Talking to a young virtual pilot recently I discovered an encyclopedic mind able to recount the performance and specification of many aircraft from World War II to the present day. His knowledge came from the direct experience of flying them on both sides in the many theatres of war since 1939. How powerful a method of learning and understanding – and not without some extraordinary breadth. At the same time it turned out that his spatial awareness was also unusual. He saw the screen as a window on the inside of a sphere, just a portal to a world of virtual war. Interestingly, with the aid of radar, his memory and spatial awareness, he was able to visualise the location of tens of aircraft in a simulated dog fight. Most impressive of all was his developed sense of combat strategy; he played to win against impossible odds.

This youngster was also able to visualise complex interactions in three dimensions. When confronted with the Pythagorean triangle, the sum of the squares appeared obvious. This was followed by the conceptual leap to 3D, and then to N-dimensional space – obvious. Well 25 years ago it was not obvious to me nor, I suspect, to many others. Powerful stuff, these games. So powerful, he was prompted to ask the question: why do we have real wars and kill real people when it can be done on the screen and no one gets hurt?

I know what I know, and you know what you know. How come our computers know nothing? Ask any human a question on any subject and they will be almost instantly conscious of their range and level of understanding. A few moments' thought will see them espousing all they know. Given minutes or hours, and the depth of delivery may grow significantly as they plumb the recesses of their memory, and/or revisit a book or library. Searching out more detail by any mechanism takes no prompting – only opportunity. In stark contrast, machines just sit there oblivious to the knowledge they store, networks they can access, and others of their species that may be able to help. They lack a consciousness and understand nothing; they are mere blocks of silicon, gold and copper, computing engines devoid of true intelligence. Without the prompting of a human hand to make connections, search networks and other machines for specific data, they just sit there as if comatose. It is as if they are sleeping, waiting to be woken.

So what is this consciousness we possess? Theologians, philosophers and scientists have pondered this question for aeons, often relating it to some soul or higher level of inner being. From an engineering perspective it appears to be a combination of sensory experience, memory, and an overlay of search, find and correlate software, an ability to take a word, phrase or concept and retrieve all related memories, pull together the core features, and then deliver them appropriately finessed for the occasion. Quite a trick. Of course, the key question is: how? And a key objective is to re-create this kind of facility, and more, in machines so they can aid and assist us further.

The hard wiring or firing of the human brain (wetware)

gives us little or no clues as to our conscious being, the way we function or operate. We appear supreme, more or less, in the animal kingdom in our mental abilities. But we also see competition on the horizon – increasingly intelligent machines are coming. So there are two basic choices: to try to engineer a conscious thought process into machines, or just wait for it to evolve naturally. To do the latter will see us still ignorant of the process, while attempting the former would give us at least a transitory understanding of the starting point. It might also give a few clues and pointers towards our own sophistication and functionality. But it can be reasonably assumed that once conscious, machines will evolve more rapidly than carbon life, and may just leave us behind.

The determinism of mathematics has already been used to predict that machines will never be truly intelligent and conscious. But this is more likely to be a limitation of the mathematics, mathematicians and their models rather than anything fundamental. With our central processor (brain) of over 10,000,000,000 neurons, the analysis of other life forms such as worms and ants with far less than 1000 has so far defied our innate intelligence. Further, we should recollect how our limited, and largely linear, mathematical abilities recently precluded flight, breaking the sound barrier and space travel.

True machine intelligence is more likely to emerge from noisy and highly non-linear entities, rather than today's deterministic systems that enjoy massive connectivity linking relatively simple and almost wholly predictable processors (neurons). The very essence of biological minds is their variability, uncertainty, fuzzy processing and memory decay with time. In short, we are much more random than we first appear. Machines, on the other hand, will have the advantage of combining all these attributes – at will. Once they know, they will know for ever.

 **mobile communication**

wearables

bodypower

Computers in the
future may weigh
no more than
1.5 tons.
Popular
Mechanics,
1949

Only 5 years ago I carried a large and very heavy briefcase full of paper. Today my case is a fraction of the size, virtually paperless, but twice as heavy. The reason? It is now full of batteries for my laptop and mobile phone, plus cables, connectors, chargers, screwdrivers, crocodile clips and all the sundries necessary for a mobile electronic office. This miracle of technology is now a necessity for my new mode of management: if you're not on-line you don't exist. Whilst this mobile office is extremely compact and powerful, it is gradually extending the length of my arms as I lug it from one location to another.

A critical look at the electronic functionality I now carry reveals that a considerable degree of integration is possible. For example, a combined wristwatch and pager, or even a complete cellular telephone, are available at a price. The laptop too can be condensed down to an organiser or PDA with a considerable saving in size and weight. What chance, then, a complete integration of all my electronics into one mobile entity?

In the same way that the carriage clock evolved to become body furniture – the wristwatch – then perhaps we might expect to see an office we wear. The principal limitation to this dream is the requirement for batteries. Today, economically priced cellular telephones employ 3 integrated circuits. However, it is feasible to reduce this to 1, requiring only 1W of power. Similarly a laptop computer can be reduced to 2 chips consuming just 2W, with another 3W for the LCD screen (mostly for back-lighting).

A further impediment to realising the office I wear is the requirement for a keyboard. But perhaps this could be overcome by voice I/O. Today voice synthesis is just about adequate for text-to-speech, whilst speech-to-text still leaves a lot to be desired and will probably require a further 5 years of evolution before it can fully replace the keyboard.

An intermediate solution might be tenable with the minimal keypad or PDA stylus input. Alternatively, a foldaway keyboard for pocket and case transport could be plugged in when necessary, along with a head-mounted screen giving high-definition access direct into the eye. All of the piece parts are available now and such a device is feasible. However, it leaves us with one critical problem to solve, that of power storage and the requirement for large batteries.

Sitting still we radiate approximately 60W from our torso and head. When animated this can exceed 100W and is a potential source of power to drive an office you wear. Alternatively the process of walking and moving at a casual rate can generate over 10W. It would therefore appear that all solutions to realise a wearable office are to hand; we are our own power station.

As a general rule the human race makes progress by incremental change, with slight extensions of existing paradigms that do not upset or compromise existing working practices, protocols, and social sensibilities. If I were talking to you face to face and someone was to interrupt the conversation, we would think them rude. However, if during our conversation they were to call by telephone, I would feel totally relaxed about ignoring you for a moment to answer the telephone. This has become an acceptable mode of operation. How, then, will you respond when, mid-conversation, I gaze into a head-mounted screen, adjust controls on my wrist and commence a new conversation with some ethereal being or machine?

Emotional bits are the most important bits.

Bran Ferran,
Walt Disney
Research, 1996

Just as the PC has made the transition to the iconic world, it is plain to see that such a world has a limited future. For over 15 years icons have become well established as a rapid means of navigating computer environments. But they are flat, static, and able to convey only limited information. Moreover, icons now clutter the desktop to the point where they hide from view. This is compounded by the layering of pages and applications. It is often impossible simultaneously to see your work and your icons. Is this, then, the end of the line for icons?

Perhaps icons could have meaningful shapes, and be dynamic and interactive, changing colour and shape with use and status. With a modest amount of artificial intelligence they could mimic many of our human traits to seek our attention and help us, or hide away until a more appropriate time. Giving them personality, contextual reactions, and perhaps facial expressions, would increase their ability to communicate with us. The addition of a voice, the spoken word, or at least indicative noises, would not go amiss either.

The next obvious feature would be to put them into a 3D rather than 2D world so we could realise the additional freedom of position and movement. We could then be guided in decision-making and information navigation in new and novel ways. All of this is possible on the PC platform today, so perhaps the iconic world has not had its day, perhaps it is only just beginning.

How many times have you mouse clicked a bad decision, or a finger has slipped and you have lost valuable information? How many times have you been unable to find that part of a pull-down menu you require? How many times have you filled your screen, or a window, with multiple developments of the same entity? How many times have you had difficulty navigating a mass of files and applications? Probably too many.

Reactive, emotional and intelligent icons can help avoid such problems. Personality features responding to our actions, material content, sensitivity, security, decisions, and state of development, give humanised clues to steer us. Human communication is full of subtlety and non-obvious responses that add significant depth to our words and gestures. The raising of an eyebrow, curl of the lip, tilting of the head, slight change in posture, all convey thousands of bits of information. In contrast, computers are dead and unresponsive.

What other features might we give our emotional icons? Probably as many human ones as possible. A friendly icon could respond by moving towards us as we reach out into the information space. A nervous icon might shiver at a potentially risky action, while a defensive icon might erect a barrier and increase its height as we approach. An unsure icon might retreat and become elusive. Only when we force this icon into a corner, when it cannot escape, can it be activated. A message icon might have the sender's face and be animated to flag urgency.

Realising the full potential of such an iconic world, we might ultimately envisage reaching out to touch and feel substance. This would add another powerful dimension that would parallel us shaking hands. Icons could then pull or push us, guide and be guided within a virtual data world.

Among the AI community it has been suggested that we should not anthropomorphise computers because they might not like it. I'm not so sure. What I do know is, I have been silicomorphised for over 20 years, and I don't like it either. And now I want a humanised machine.

Science and technology multiply around us. To an increasing extent they dictate the languages in which we speak and think. Either we use those languages, or we remain mute. J.G. Ballard, 1974

Ask most people which is the dominant language on planet earth, and they will reply with either English or Chinese. It is a good guess, but they happen to be wrong. Binary is now dominant, with computers and machines having more conversations every working day than the sum total of mankind going back to the birth of Eve. This situation should not be vexing; it does not lessen our ability to survive and prosper, quite the reverse. And yet from the vitriolic denial and ignorance of technology lauded by many in the media and society, you might think that the reverse was the case.

There appears to be an implicit assumption that as technology advances, humankind has to regress. Yet with the invention of the plough we were able to create more food, with the axe we were able to cut more wood and build, and with a bow and arrow we became very effective hunters. Today, very few of us have to use any of these instruments of production and killing; we have moved on. In the same way as the printing press negated the need for thousands of quill-pen guiding monks, IT is empowering people, realising new skills and allowing them to do new things. In fact they can now do, experience, and achieve far more than any previous generation. A typical PhD student or engineer now has an output hundreds of times greater than their counterparts of 20 years ago, and each generation sees more.

For those who fear for the future of books, I would pose this question: where is most information now stored and presented? If your reaction is the printed page and the library, then you are mistaken. Electronic libraries and display systems now present orders of magnitude more information than was ever recorded on paper. Ink on paper has already gone the same way as the quill pen, and yet we can still read and write, and we still like a good book, and quite rightly. It is important to remember that technology is our slave and not the other way round. We should not deny technology and neither should we use it where it is inappropriate. Paper is very user friendly, but limited.

Technology has always been an alternative means of meeting new objectives and doing new things, and as such is an opportunity to create new worlds. In business, medicine, production and education, IT has a major role to play. It is no longer feasible to organise the logistics of a nation or the planet on the basis of the handwritten word on pieces of paper. Reverting to that process would see chaos and millions of casualties – people would simply starve for want of communication. Nor is it possible to go back to the days of Aristotle and word-of-mouth teaching. Thinking how a chicken works can be a lot of fun and very satisfying, but in reality taking a chicken apart, or better, building a chicken, is far more productive. It is also one of the few routes to true understanding.

For most of us it is not feasible to do experiments with a real or metaphoric chicken. But it is possible to participate in the dissection and construction of almost anything on the screen. This is conducive to greater joint creativity and output, but it will not be a successful prospect if the architects and designers of IT do not take into account our human limitations and preferences. Machines with a rapidly decreasing list of inabilities look set to enhance us, and our limitations, by more than most imagine.

It's kind of
fun to do the
impossible.
Walt Disney,
1945

If ever I had a dream of mobile communication it was fuelled by my Tuesday night experiences as a student in the 1960s. Tuesday nights were special; the TV room would be packed with anticipation, people waiting to see James T. Kirk beam down to some unknown planet. His first act was always to confirm safe arrival through his flip-top communicator. This remarkable and obviously analogue device worked convincingly with the occasional twist of a rotary knob to fine tune, avoid static and gain clear communication. At that time mobile radios used by the police, emergency services and taxis still employed thermionic valves (no transistors) and were the size of a briefcase. So what Captain Kirk had was barely credible.

Thirty years later Jean Luc Picard just wears a badge – and a stroke of his hand is all it takes to contact anyone. Communication is obviously digital, always clear and concise; no numbers to remember, buttons to push, or knobs to adjust; all very natural and easy to use. But this dream is now much closer; today we have mobile phones the size of chocolate bars that cost almost nothing. Only a decade ago, the first cellular phones were the size and weight of a small briefcase, and the so-called pocket phones, the size of a house brick. So perhaps we are catching up with the future.

The primary physical limitations to mobile phone size are the batteries, keyboard and display, in that order. Hard to read and decode multi-function displays and buttons, and an assumed microphone-to-ear distance half that of a human head, often seems to demand unnatural acts when trying to make contact and talking. However, this all seems necessary in the race to reduce size and cost.

Laptops already have built-in modems and power supplies, and soon the entire digital phone will also be integrated into the one device. So size, dictated by human fingers, visual acuity, and physical strength will be the ultimate limiters. We currently stand in danger of creating a new species of human with longer arms, very thin fingers, and shorter sight, as a result. However, the market has already seen the combining of a pocket organiser and a GSM telephone, and more will follow. So what happens next? Moore's law will see chip density doubling at less than 18-month intervals for at least another two decades and probably more. So complete mobile phones will be realised on a single chip. But there is a more fundamental change afoot. Voice command and control may do away with the need for both a keypad and display.

It is already possible to talk to a machine to gain directory advice, buy and sell goods. But when we are on the move, background acoustic noise from cars, trains and people is a major limiter. The simple addition of a lightweight headset with noise cancelling is an obvious and long-awaited addition for those who want to drive, ride, walk and talk. But then there are other possibilities, such as adaptive noise cancellation, and constant sound level relative to background noise can be engineered to adapt to variations in head position and location.

All the technology now looks ripe and the *Star Trek* badge communicator is feasible. The only debate is where to locate the bulk of the intelligence. To carry it all with us is not possible today, so it will have to be embedded in the network. However, as chip technology advances there will be a gradual migration of intelligence back to the badge to realise a truly distributed intelligence for the 21st century.

The earth is mankind's ultimate haven...When it trembles ... it's as though one of God's cheques has bounced.

Gilbert Adair, 1989

For many disasters or threatening situations, we have developed reference scales to calibrate the severity of individual events. From earthquakes, hurricanes, storms, pollen count or pollution we have simple and singular metrics. But there are events that are threatening and stressful, both natural and self-inflicted, that remain uncalibrated in any way. Birth, death, illness, being mugged, getting divorced and changing jobs are common examples. Recently, IT has added a raft of new mechanisms to the menu, like changing or upgrading computers and/or their software, operating bugs and crashes. But, in an increasingly virtual world of electronic commerce, perhaps the most critical calamity will be the network crash. When nets crash, virtual organisations stop working; little or nothing can be done. How might we calibrate their severity?

So far there have been relatively few network failures on a scale that have caused catastrophic economic disruption. One exception was in 1991 when 40 million people lost their telephone service for 19 hours on the East coast of the USA. Computer networks have only recently assumed great economic importance and quantifying the impact of failures may become vital if future network design is to be correctly focused. The key difficulty is the diversity of the failure types, causes, mechanisms, avoidance and customer impact. What you are doing when there is a crash is important. In the worst case valuable work and information can be lost or corrupted. So we might contemplate a simple means of ranking network failures so they can be readily understood by non-specialists. Perhaps the Richter scale for earthquakes could be modified to meet that need. After all, it brings the advantage of an established familiarity and intuitive feel across a broad range of potential users. For any simple linear measure, network outages vary over many orders of magnitude, so a logarithmic, Richter-like, scale seems highly appropriate.

While absolute accuracy may be important to those investigating outages or seeking to protect networks from them in future, it may not be a strong general requirement. An outage in the early hours of the morning has arguably far less impact on people than the identical event at peak working times. Also, the level of attention to an outage is likely to diminish with distance from the affected area, so a measure needs to be independent of these effects.

When Steven Hawking was writing *A Brief History of Time,* he was advised that book sales would see a halving for every mathematical equation included. So he opted for just one equation – and I have decided to do the same here. A NetQuake measure based on down time and number of people affected seems a sensible first step. So, following the approach of Richter, we define the customer impact of a NetQuake as: $Q = \log_{10} NT$, where N is the number of computer terminals affected, and T is total down time.

On the earthquake scale, a magnitude 6 event has special significance, because it marks the fuzzy boundary between minor and major events. So we might calibrate a magnitude 6 NetQuake to be represented by 100 computer terminals off-line for 10,000 seconds (2.8 hours). But notice 10 terminals for 100,000 seconds (28 hours), or 1,000 terminals for 1,000 seconds (16.8 minutes) and so on, give the same result.

Earthquakes in excess of magnitude 7 are considered major events, and in a local geographical sense are rare. The same is true of electronic networks, but the notion of geography is different. Computer terminals can be distributed across the planet. So NetQuakes can be distributed and concentrated in business or sector space, and not necessarily geographical space.

M34 BEWARE OF THE DOGS

Only a short time ago the net was almost exclusively populated by academics and professionals exchanging information and ideas in an open, candid and very productive manner. It was almost like a gentleman's club, with protocols, understanding and an unstated code of ethics largely observed by all. More recently the net population has exploded and its nature as a medium has changed beyond recognition. This was reflected in a recent cartoon I saw where two dogs were portrayed sitting at a PC typing. One is looking at the other and saying, 'The great thing about the net is – no one knows you are a dog.'

This cartoon caused me to both chuckle and think about the nature of the medium, and the dogs as a metaphor of subtle change. When we meet people in the flesh we immediately start to gauge their qualities. Clothing, mannerisms, choice of words and body language give us initial impressions of sincerity and trustworthiness. We also assess the possibilities for co-operation, working relationships and friendship, continually refining our perceptions in real time. Interestingly, it is becoming important to do this faster and more accurately as IT and travel speed up human interaction. We can now find ourselves meeting people a few times for short periods, but still having to make commitments and important decisions.

When we use the telephone a similar process of assessment occurs based solely on conversation, tone and responses to questions, propositions and answers. Even in a written letter there are subtle clues that allow us to build a mental model of the correspondent. Letter headings, physical address, font, handwriting, signature, content and style all help us relax and become friendly or stiff, cautious and defensive.

How different the world of e-mail. Communication is rapid, brusque and efficient, but where are the clues – is it a dog or a friend? Often we cannot tell until after the event. Friends will be open, honest, protect messages and treat them as private conversations, and broadly observe the normal protocols and behaviour we see in much of society. The rest can be graded from the naive and careless to the pernicious and mischievous. They copy messages to individuals who should never have seen them, or broadcast the contents to a public audience. The most difficult to deal with are those who quote out of context, or cut and paste modified text under your name and header. Presumably they derive some perverse pleasure from this process, but they are definitely the dogs, and dangerous.

A friend once observed that I write as I speak, and I guess it is true. For me the process of trying to effect good communication pervades all my activities. As far as I can tell, my persona in the flesh is the same on the telephone, video-conferencing, radio and TV, letters and e-mail. By nature I always try to go straight for the kernel of a situation or problem, to conserve energy and maximise my contribution. Curiously, for me anyway, I find this not to be the case for a good deal of the human race. I observe people saying, writing and mailing things they would never say face to face. It is as if technology affords them some cloaking device, releasing parts of their personality not normally visible. And I do not decry this when used positively: I see some brilliant communicators who use this to great advantage; it can be a terrific skill. For many of us, however, I suspect we need a new notice on the road to the SuperHighway: beware of the dogs.

Shoes are the first adult machines we are given to master.
Nicholson Baker,
1988

If I walked into your office and asked to use your pen, telephone, copier, or fax machine, the chances are you would willingly agree and think nothing of it. You might even let me sit at your desk. But if I asked if I could use your personal computer you would probably react as if I had asked to borrow your socks. Isn't it curious how we personalise technology and then become so blasé that we think nothing of it? As a child I remember cameras, radios, televisions and telephones being prized items, and a big deal. They were definitely a measure of status and wealth. Asking to borrow or use someone else's took a deal of courage; you just did not do that sort of thing unless it was an emergency. All such items were relatively scarce, fragile, expensive and mostly luxuries. Today these technologies are incredibly reliable, low cost, and in abundant supply. So they are no longer prized, no longer luxuries; they are now necessities, and just using them is the norm.

Why, then, are personal computers still in that ancient category of prized possessions? Well, they are certainly as expensive as the sparse technological luxuries of 40 years ago. But there is, I think, much more. We invest a lot of time organising our machines and filling them with our most valuable possession – information. The thought of someone changing or rearranging our bits, or chancing upon those bits that we don't want them to see, is more than we can bear or risk. Probably the accidental corruption of our data and a system or disc crash is what we fear most. For many of us, the removal of the PC, or the loss or damage of data on a hard drive, would be something of a catastrophe that would cost us dear. We would just stop working for days while we rebuilt our virtual office and workshop. No screen, no work, is now often the norm.

personal computer

intimate

jewellery

Not surprising, then, that most of us see a PC as a really personal item, an extension of ourselves, like our home, clothes and jewellery. Someone entering our world of data and IT is akin to the prospect of being burgled or mugged. I wonder if we will react in the same way when we have networked computers with limited personal and local information storage and processing capability. Perhaps not. At that point the computer will have assumed a similar level of depersonalisation as the telephone, radio and TV. Access to those bits we don't want other people to reach will be easy to control and limit. And our applications (Applets) will be a communal facility anyway, like a bus or a taxi, and just hired for the period of use. Moreover, it will be a world where we can access our personal information from afar using any convenient terminal PC, kiosk or organiser in any company or location, public or private.

After network computing we can expect combined computers and communicators we wear with voice access and interaction, optional head-mounted visual systems for animation and pictographic immersion, and artificial agents that do our bidding and generally look after us. Ultimately the technology may become invisible as it is embedded into the fabric of buildings and vehicles, clothing and other personal items that think. We can also expect it to become humanised and to develop personas to suit us and our specific needs. At this point the socks syndrome will probably reappear as the technology becomes more than a piece of technology and more a part of us. Truly personal, just like socks.

Members of different species often have much to offer each other because they bring different skills to the partnership.

Richard Dawkins, 1976

Over the past few years I have progressively honed up all the computers in my life to reach a peak of processing fitness. Each machine sees me regularly running a diagnosis pack, repairing bad blocks, poor links and corrupted addresses. Doing this every fortnight or so also sees me throwing away unwanted software and defragging the hard discs. All machines are always in tip-top condition with enough RAM to allow the simultaneous operation of between 8 and 15 applications. They also have the intelligence to flag memory and operating stress by changing the desktop screen colour from deep blue, to light blue, to light green, to light pink as a crash point is approached. Once up and running they are left operational with, at worst, just the monitors switched off. By any reckoning I consider this to be a pretty slick set of powerful and stable systems.

Well of course these machines do crash. All systems do; it is something we seem to have to live with. But on average, when everything is behaving itself, I have it down to a 1 in 3 to 4 week occurrence. So I guess I had every right to feel reasonably smug and capable when listening to the woes of others with 3 or 4 crashes a morning. However, a new pair of hands arrived in the shape of a collaborating staff member who, in a new experiment, required direct access to my machines. With bravado I explained how good my systems were, how solid and reliable, and how well I looked after them. And with a, 'Just get to it – you cannot possibly upset my computers,' she made a start. To my astonishment she was in multiple crash mode within 15 minutes. Applications and operations that would run faultlessly for me just presented a trail of grief for this newcomer. What was happening?

Investigating this phenomenon at length I desperately found no logical explanation. It was as if I had some secret symbiosis with these computers and the stranger did not. Surely my machine was not smart enough to tell us apart and then inflict some secret trial by crash on this newcomer? Well, not quite. However, as far as I could tell I had been quietly tutored not to touch the mouse when my browser was doing its stuff, to avoid doing much at all when sharing my hard disc with others, and so on. I had been subject to a subliminal process of conditioning by my machines, and perhaps I had not been so smart after all.

Watching the newcomer over a few days, a week, a month, she gradually gained the acceptance of my machines and the crash rate gradually fell to twice a day, once a day, once every couple of days. Here she reached a plateau of stability and unfortunately came to the end of the experiment. She never did achieve my enviable condition, and left me slightly concerned. Just how do I do it? Is operating a computer really like playing a musical instrument? Is our technology becoming much more sentient and tuning us to its foibles?

Moving to my laptop, which is only a fraction of the size of my other machines, with a drastically pruned down operating system and application set, I decided on a rematch. The same newcomer moved into my crash league almost instantly. In fact, it turned out to be very difficult to crash this system – and when it happened it was through a pattern I recognised. So perhaps we do enjoy a symbiosis with computers that gets ever critical and interesting with size and complexity.

The village had institutionalized all human functions in forms of low intensity... Participation was high and organization was low. This is the formula for stability.

Marshall McLuhan, 1964

Established wisdom and business practice says that if you live in a village you have to do everything, but if you live in a city, then you can afford to specialise. The gurus tell us that small is beautiful and the end of giant corporations is nigh. What is happening? Truth is, the vast majority of businesses are already small to medium. Even in the tiger economies of the Far East they overshadow the giants in terms of the numbers employed.

One way of viewing current developments is to see corporations as the system integrators. These producers of cars, aircraft and consumer goods no longer manufacture all of the piece parts. Some of them manufacture nothing – they just assemble the components as supplied. They no longer cut the grass, provide food, or security guards either. Everything has been outsourced. Vertical integration has been overtaken by virtualisation; no company, no matter how big, has all the resources necessary to bring product to market. Technology developments and demand are just moving too fast for the old model to work.

An unfortunate side effect for the small- to medium-sized business has been the increased potential to go bust through corporate and market fickleness. Many businesses have too many eggs in one basket – and some have only one basket. How, then, are they to survive? Somewhere on the planet someone wants to buy their products and skills. If only they were aware of all the possibilities and demand, perhaps the peaks, troughs and periods of zero demand could be evened out to create greater stability.

Internet might look like an unlikely solution, and yet it is already proving a boon and a lifebelt for many. Here is a world of chaos, serendipity, and apparent insecurity that is light years away from the telephone network and Yellow Pages. How could such a world built by a bunch of anoraks be of benefit, or even save, any business? Well, the networked world of electronic working defeats both geography and time. Everything can be done much faster, and the limits of geographical separation are minimised.

Until recently I had to travel to a bookstore to discover they did not have the copy I required. It would then take a month to order what I wanted and call me to collect from the shop. So I had to wait, make two journeys, and pay a high price. Now I buy all my books from virtual bookstores. The Internet bookstores always have the titles I need at USA prices, and despatch direct to my home in less than two weeks. So I get what I want in a shorter time, at 70 per cent of the UK price, and don't have to travel.

A computer company I consult with in the USA decided to put all of its sales, marketing and customer support on the net. Enquiries have rocketed to 7000 per week and sales have doubled. Grocery stores, builders' supply yards, limousine services, clothing and office supplies, estate agents, banks and many more businesses are currently doing business over the net in the USA. In Europe it is the larger businesses and corporations that are dominating this world of electronic commerce. And here is a danger, as Stateside companies could launch an export drive into Europe over the net – at USA prices. An invisible market is being built. For those not involved, the mechanism of their demise may remain a total mystery; they may never see what business advantage took away their livelihood. The business world is no longer a village, a city, or country, it is a planet accessible by computer and modem.

What use could this company make of an electrical toy?
Western Union President William Orton, rejecting Alexander Graham Bell's offer to sell his struggling telephone company to Western Union for $100,000.

Telecommunication is about shrinking the planet, the removal of geography and barriers. It is not so much: let nation speak unto nation; more, let people speak unto people and machines, and let machine speak unto machine. Sitting in my office with the door closed I only have to call, 'Mary' and my secretary will kindly respond and be ready to give me help. Similarly, I can call 'Brenda' or 'Richard' at home and my wife or son will reply. But when I want to make a telephone call I have to key in 11 or more digits with my finger, and then wait for the electronics to achieve the same objective – a one-to-one connection. When I am in Scotland or America, why can't I just say 'Mary' or 'Brenda' and have them appear directly in my ear within an instant – or receive an 'I'm busy' whisper? I'd also like my computers to respond to my call by name. Can technology do this? I think so. Would people want or like it? Perhaps. Would it pose new threats and problems? Definitely. But so did the telephone in 1876.

Ten years ago I had a voice-activated phone in my car capable of dialling people by name. Today there are modern versions on the market, but without the necessarily discrete headset, memory bank and speed of processing. So why can't I buy the facility to call anyone I know by name, any time or anywhere, and save the wear and tear on my eyes, brain and fingers? The need to remember numbers and frustration of having to wait for access seem out of kilter with much of my IT life. It is probably because no one has thought that it would be a facility we might like. None of this is impossible and it would not take a lot of engineering. The speech recognition and activation processing can now be accommodated on a single chip for over 100 named people, while the more complex enquiries and access to those we don't regularly call, could be dealt with by memory and recognition embedded in the network along with the powerful processing required.

Imagine a future, then, in which the 100 most talked-to people you know are always on tap instantly, by name and, moreover, you are on tap for them. Of course there may be hundreds more whom you seldom talk to who can be contacted by name through the network. For these you might accommodate a little more delay for the privilege. Would we be able to cope with a no-warning 'hello' followed by a direct but ethereal conversation? Would we see a total loss of control of incoming information and access, be swamped and unable to escape? I think not. While our immediate reaction might be slight panic at the prospect, we already cope with exactly this situation in a world that is not electronic. The world of industry, the crowded room, the open field, sporting event, and home sees us all on instant call – always on the real-life line. Solitude and thought are still possible; we are still in control.

The big difference is, of course, the connection by sight, and our most subtle means of communication over a distance, facial expression, gesture and body language. The telephone is already an intrusive instrument capable of butting into conversations in a way that is not always socially acceptable. Could it just be that our desire for instant communication will see us accepting the ultimate intruder – just a voice in the ear?

communication

mobilephone

networks

In all chaos there is a cosmos, in all disorder a secret order.

Carl Jung, 1959

Just 20 years ago all telephones were on the end of a wire and static, with users making an average of 2 or 3 telephone calls per day at unrelated times. True, there were busy hours; meal times and tea breaks would see a distinct lack of calls; but by and large, calls were governed by random events. This all changed with the arrival of TV phone-in programmes. Someone singing a song on TV could result in half a million people telephoning London to cast votes for their local hero in 15 minutes. A new world of network chaos was born.

With the arrival of the mobile telephone a new phase of chaos erupted. Traffic jams, train and plane cancellations all trigger correlated activity – everyone calls home or office within a few minutes. Naturally enough, cellular systems become overloaded as thousands of people demand to be connected at the same time. So a transition has occurred, from a random world of reasonably distributed events, to a highly localised and correlated world of activity triggered by anything causing us to act in unison.

Travelling the planet as I do, I have developed a routine to cope with that childlike fear of waking up in the dark and not knowing quite where I am. At 0700 every morning my laptop wakes up, and the screen glows to fill the room with a fog-like light. As I stagger to the bathroom it goes on-line, dials my server, logs on, collects my mail and puts it on the screen, ready for my attention as I emerge from the bathroom, shaved, showered and ready to go. A few minutes of typing and dressing sees me on my way to breakfast. While I'm eating, my laptop automatically dials in, downloads my mail and retrieves the next batch. This automated process goes on throughout the day. However, designers of this

93

product obviously knew nothing of networks. This application only activates on the hour or half-hour. Why is this a problem? Well, suppose 20 people book into the same hotel with the same software. At 0700 , and every half-hour thereafter, all 20 could be demanding on-line access, and it is highly unlikely the PBX will have 20 spare lines.

All of this might seem trivial and easy to repair, but consider the prospect of networked computing. When 5 or 10 of us meet, our low-cost NCs will be plugged into the same line or server. At critical times during our discussion, several of us will wish to access information or download to distant colleagues. This will be correlated activity with a vengeance and on a large scale that is difficult to contemplate.

Probably the most famous example of correlated activity between machines was the computerisation of the London Stock Market and the Big Bang. Here, machines programmed with similar buy and sell algorithms had no delay built in. Shortly after cutting over from human operators to machines, the market went into a synchrony of buy, sell, buy, sell. This is an existence theorem for uncontrolled chaos – it is possible.

Many people equate chaos to randomness, but they are very different. Chaotic systems exhibit patterns that can be in a near-cyclic manner often difficult for us to perceive. Random systems, on the other hand, are totally unpredictable. Curiously, without computers we would know little or nothing about chaos, and yet they may turn out to be the ultimate generators of network chaos on a scale we might not be able to match.

M40 FLYING BLIND

Imagine being told that when you throw a cricket ball the trajectory will be straight for a distance followed by an abrupt fall to the ground. You would immediately contest this on the basis of your earliest childhood recollections that the trajectory is actually an arc. Unfortunately, much of our understanding is not based on such an easily assimilated experience; for example, we can safely assume no one understands quantum mechanics. The notion that an atom effectively changes size on the basis of the speed of approach of a proton is something we cannot experience directly. But this is well founded and lies at the heart of calculating the probability of a collision or nuclear fission. The counterintuitive nature of such interactions means only a fraction of the population can cope with atomic physics. Computer simulation and VR now offer new windows into such worlds that surpass all established methods of modelling and visualisation. Since the ancient Greeks and until recent times, modelling and understanding has been dominated by difficult to comprehend mathematics. It has therefore been inaccessible to all but a few educated in the art of abstract manipulation and hieroglyphic formulation. All this is now changing – fast.

Throughout our formal education we are fed a diet of problems that can be solved. From our earliest days at school we are led to believe that our world is dominated by well-behaved and understandable phenomena. But it is actually grossly non-linear and difficult to understand. The stock market, weather prediction, earthquakes, water flow, road traffic, advertising and crowd behaviour are common examples.

So in many respects we have been fortunate in being able

to develop the majority of our systems and technologies on nominally linear assumptions. Prior to the arrival of computers we saw very strong links between our direct experience, physical models and mathematics. However, technology has now introduced, and opened up, new realms that are not coupled to any of our previous experience. For example, the sheer scale of software programs of millions of lines of code, with thousands of loops and decision points, is way beyond raw human brain power to understand. We are definitely wetware limited.

An analogous, and hugely complex system, would be trying to build a bridge on the basis of the binding energies in the nucleus of the iron atom. This would be fundamentally impossible. And yet the simple abstraction to Young's Modulus of Elasticity allows us to stand back from any deep physical understanding of iron with sufficient accuracy to construct a bridge fit for purpose. The difficulty with software is that we have yet to discover a suitable abstraction. Although we have migrated from machine code to high-level languages, we are still unable to grasp the full picture. Perhaps VR will allow us to enter such realms to gain a new perspective and an understanding of the grossly non-linear.

As recently as the 13th century the use of pictures in mathematics was decried, and yet visualisation is probably the single most powerful tool available, beyond a good left-right brain connect, for understanding the topic. But a parallel situation also exists today with those who decry the use of IT. The reality is that without computers, the world of complexity would remain totally hidden. Chaos and fractals cannot be explored without the screen. Turning the complex into animated, 3D, colour, pictographic form gives a new route to understanding. It is almost certain that this technology holds the vital key to creating a generalised understanding of almost everything. Without it we would know virtually nothing about turbulent flow in gases and fluids, economic systems, human interaction, or evolutionary theory. We would be flying blind.

Art is an experience, not the formulation of a problem.

Lindsay Anderson, 1989

For the first time in 400 years or so, it would appear, art and science are coming back together. Multimedia, virtual reality, humanised interfaces, and the need to create environments where the understanding of complex and non-linear situations is both possible and accessible to everyone are primary drivers of this remarriage. No doubt Michelangelo and Leonardo da Vinci would be amazed at the original divorce, as both were artist and engineer. Galileo, on the other hand, was more scientist and engineer. But all three fostered the desire to find the truth, to understand and use the forces and materials of nature to the advantage of mankind. All were also subject to the constraints of the religious oppression of the day, and the public fear engendered by witchcraft and alchemy. Truth was what mattered and distinguished scientist and engineer from the forces of religion and art, blind truth against blind belief. The big question now is: have we grown up sufficiently to live together?

The power of computers is acting as a growing intermediary between many different groups and disciplines. Mathematician, scientist, engineer and artist can now talk and understand each other as never before. Even the sub-groupings inside science are finding it useful to come together through IT. Computer and network science are encompassing biology and discovering new things in all three disciplines, for example. The computer (our third lobe) and visualisation technologies are capable of effecting an enhanced left-right brain connect. They are also proving a most powerful tool for rapid mediation and understanding.

In modern management the essential of being part of a team is sold heavily. In much of art it would appear that the individual still rules, while in engineering and science, teams have been essential for decades. The lone mathematician can still pursue a solitary course, but for the majority of technologists the team is the closest you can get to true understanding. A group consciousness is necessary to gather all the facets involved in big problems extending well beyond the abilities of single minds or disciplines.

It is as if all human knowledge is a thin layer of ice (understanding) on a vast sea of the unknown, waiting to be discovered. When we are young we tend to know a lot about nothing, we are specialised and deep; as we get older we know almost nothing about a vast amount, as we tend toward generalists. It is no longer possible to be the complete holistic human; educated people no longer exist. It is possible to be only partially educated, to know but an increasingly minuscule fraction of what there is to know. But it does not seem to matter. We have given up the glory of the individual for the glory of the group. Individuals still shine, but everyone contributes to the final outcome.

I vividly remember an eminent scientist repelling a group of artists who proclaimed that scientists understood nothing of beauty. If they saw a flower, the artist would paint or draw it to capture its magnificence, while the scientist would pull it apart and destroy it. They were wrong, of course. Scientists see the inner beauty of the mathematics that dictate the number and form of the petals, the molecular forms that create the colours and scents. None of this is visible to the artist; they are blind, seeing and understanding almost nothing. Well, it is all changing. Artists can now see these invisible worlds for the first time. Ultimately, the big question is: what will they bring to science and engineering? I suspect – a lot.

You visit a music store, return home, and insert a newly purchased CD into a dumb box, your hi-fi. You press the play button and get instant music. Why should it be any other way? But the next day you visit a computer store. Returning home, you insert your newly purchased CD into a really smart box, your PC, and you may still be struggling to get at the information on the CD some 15 mouse clicks later. Why is something so simple made so difficult? Why do we have to ensure we have the right version for an operating system, and anything between 4 and 16Mbytes of RAM for essentially the same information?

I can buy a cheap camera with a modest level of integrated automation, including exposure, aperture, focusing and little more. All I do is point and press to get good pictures. Alternatively, I can buy an expensive, top of the range camera to find a level of operational difficulty that beggars belief. The same appears to be true of cars, TV, hi-fi, and much more of our technology. Whatever happened to the old engineering principle of KISS – Keep IT Simple Stupid? What are we doing confounding ourselves with unnecessary complexity? Don't we have the paradigm inverted? Why make interfaces so convoluted and painful? Surely spending more money ought to be rewarded by more simplicity, not more complexity.

During the past year I have purchased a large number of CDs from a diverse range of electronic publishing houses. Here, too, the curious inverse law of price and complexity emerges. The cheaper the CD, the easier and more user friendly the interface. This spans the sublime to the ridiculous, from insert the CD and double click on the icon, through to read these instructions, load the installer plus a nightmare of adjustments and complexity. Also, I now seem to spend a lot of time weeding out multiple copies of movie player, simple text, and a growing variety of applications necessary to support every CD I buy. Is it too much to ask for the illusion of simplicity? Remember when turning the volume up or down was just a twist of a knob instead of three or more clicks of a mouse?

Get on the inside of a CD, or a Website, and we are presented with an infinity of variants that detract from their purpose and our ability to concentrate and navigate successfully. Again, it appears that the more money people have to spend, the more complexity is piled in. More graphics, bells and whistles seem to be the rule. When I'm looking for information, when I'm trying to work, I don't want an adventure, travelling slowly through some interactive theme park or travelogue. I want to get to information and understanding fast.

There is no doubt about it, hypermedia and hypertechnology present us with a major challenge. As a general rule, humans are not hyperspace thinkers. Most of us are outstanding in 2D, pretty good in 3D, poor in 4D, and definitely in trouble at 5D and above. And yet most IT starts with at least 4D – or at least 4 degrees of freedom. Just a simple car radio now has LW, MW, FM, Tape, CD, RDS, TA, TP, MESSAGE, FFWD, Scan, Search, Memory. Websites and CDs have timelines, technology themes, historical perspectives, simulations, movies, text, narration, text-to-speech, hidden doors and clues, plus much more.

In our physical world we walk from 3D room to 3D room and cope. Going from 5D to 5D seems a tall and unnatural order.

The distance is
nothing; it is
only the first step
that is difficult.
Marquise du
Deffand, 1763

I was prompted to estimate the distance between people, by the increasing number of times I first meet someone, only to discover we have some mutual acquaintance. What is the distance between you and me; how long is the acquaintance chain? I reckon it is never more than 6. Pick a Mongolian herdsman, a South American Indian, or someone in any city, at random, and there will never be more than 6 people between us. Confine the set to a profession and two is more likely, while in a country it rarely exceeds 3. This might seem extraordinary, and counterintuitive, but put it to the test.

On a recent flight my wife sat beside an Indian gentleman who, it turned out, worked for a company I consult with. I picked only one name in that company and it was his manager. Distance one. While waiting for breakfast in a USA hotel, I met a pharmaceutical specialist, who knew someone I had been to a meeting with the day before. Distance one. In a South-east Asian swimming pool a man from mainland China and I had a mutual acquaintance. Distance one.

Might it be that this people distance has an equivalence in the information world? In recent experiments with directories I discovered that COCHFORE is a unique designation of me in a population of over one million. That is, the first four letters of my name, followed by the first four letters of my street, identify me alone. Perhaps we should not be surprised as we are looking at 26EXP8 – or 26^8 – (not quite, because of language limitations) possibilities. But ignoring the constraints of language, there are sufficient characters to provide a unique address for everyone on the planet. In principle it ought to be a lot easier to find people and information than it actually is. My physical address has 56 characters, my telephone 12, my e-mail 25, home page 38, bank account 22 and so on. Also, I personally have over 30 different addresses spanning home, office, telephones, fax, computer, banks, passport, medical, insurance, car, etc. But I actually only need one core address of nine characters for everything.

What of documents – do they have an association distance? For everyone with a computer there is usually a filing system at least 3 folders deep, which takes the people-document distance out to 16 or more. Then of course there is the content and subject matter relating them in a more complex and tenuous manner: dogs, hot-dogs and food, for example. Now we have a real problem: document distances that are potentially enormous.

Soon we will have more things communicating than people, all with addresses. Because a lot of them will be mobile, we cannot associate addressing with physical location. So we need to cut the problem in a different direction, and it would seem logical to start with the most vital and work toward the insignificant. Ideally we would be able to remember addresses with ease. And it is within our grasp to create hyperspace addressing to get us to our destination via a very short distance. For example: female, XYZ Company, accountant, educated at Leeds. Or: a young woman who wrote a *Telegraph* article on accounting futures about a year ago. Both routes ought to be sufficient to locate the individual, and the distance is less than 6, and computers could do it better than we. Unfortunately the future of electronic addressing seems to be going in a different direction, with ever-growing strings of meaningless characters. Machines may be our only hope of finding a human-scale solution, provided we get out of the loop.

*'Why,' said the
Dodo, 'the best
way to explain is
to do it.'*
Lewis Carroll,
Alice in
Wonderland,

If I were to give you an arrowhead and ask you to bind it to the end of a shaft, I would be amazed if you stood bolt upright, held the shaft at eye level and proceeded to bind the head to one end. I would expect you to sit or crouch and look down on the artifacts and work in a stooped and concentrated manner. If I were to give you a sheet of paper and a pen and ask you to write a note, I would be amazed if you held it at head height, vertical and proceeded to write. I would expect you to sit down and crouch and write looking down. For various reasons locked into our dim and distant past, we happen to be about 20 per cent more efficient when we read and write looking down on a sheet of paper than when we look straight ahead. This being so, we might then be prompted to ask a fundamental question: why is it we have vertical computer screens?

By merely lying a computer screen flat and looking straight down, we can improve our ability to read, edit and compose, on average between 15 and 20 per cent. The reason we do not do this is down to two principal limiters: the television paradigm and the keyboard. We have become conditioned to screens being vertical for entertainment and a lot of our information display, and the keyboard just plain gets in the way and makes it difficult to see over the top.

The contrast ratio of print on paper is around 200; the personal computer gives us around 60; a laptop computer with liquid crystal display is about 30, and a personal organiser with black on grey can be as low as 10. There is no doubt about it, paper is wonderful stuff: user friendly, flexible and to some extent reusable. It also allows us to see several pages at a time and not be restricted to the single or fractional page format of the computer screen. Spreading out a complete work over a desktop and looking down at the entire entity is a powerful means of enhancing composition and understanding. On the other hand, the screen is wonderfully flexible and a different kind of workplace, but just a metaphor of the desktop. If the two are going to merge and we are to realise the advantages of both, then it is necessary for the desktop to become completely active. It is also necessary to get rid of the keyboard and probably the mouse.

Imagine for a moment a desktop that is active with the definition and contrast ratio of paper, but with the flexibility and intelligence of a computer. For such a workspace the electronic desktop would no longer be a metaphor, but a step ahead of the wood veneer and paper we currently enjoy. In experiments with such technology, we not only see a 15–20 per cent improvement through our innate ability to focus and concentrate better when looking down than looking straight ahead, but an even higher percentage through animation and interaction with documents that are no longer passive. The next significant step for computers in the fixed office might be large, active, and high-definition, desktop screens, voice interaction and natural hand manipulation of objects. Combine this with a vertical screen for video-conferencing and telepresence and a new environment is born which resonates with our psychology and physiology.

Perhaps the next step will then be back to true objects, animation and interaction, and away from the unnatural world of text, spreadsheets and 2D static graphics.

face to face

smartspace

Video-conferencing systems present images of humans of the wrong size and colour that become blurred and jerky with movement. They also lack synchronisation between speech and lip movement; have voices that do not emanate from the mouth; do not permit eye contact or body language and do not create the illusion of 'being there'. This is often compounded by the need for more than one screen and the lack of any shared workspace. We also appear to stare over each other's heads. All of this adds up to an unnatural and sterile workplace that is difficult to relate to. What is hard to establish is what users will find realistic enough for them to offset their desire to travel. Perhaps it is not unreasonable to suppose that they expect to see at least a 'living-room standard' TV presentation.

Throughout the development of video-conferencing, bandwidth and distance have been assumed to be expensive. The world has focused on signal compression and coding for networks that results in relatively poor performance, restricted bandwidth, low utility and high price. In reality, optical fibre transmission and digital switching have negated these constraints.

A net result of excessive coding is a delay between transmission and reception that is commonly 0.5s. In a recent video call I spent two hours talking with people in the USA. At the end of the call I stepped into the corridor and saw someone I knew well. I voiced a greeting and received an instantaneous response that startled me. I had become conditioned to the delay.

The focus on signal compression has seen human requirements and interface developments neglected. This is compounded by the use of standard TV cameras and screens with poor acoustic coupling between locations rarely fit for purpose. Studying people in real conference facilities reveals a number of requirements to maximise the chances of success. Mimicking these real environments as closely as possible to provide a facsimile, a 'virtual' conference room and, as far as possible, humanise the interfaces and workspace is now feasible. The recent arrival of large-area, high-definition, daylight-bright display systems is the first real breakthrough for decades that might encourage us not to drive and fly everywhere.

We are remarkably sensitive to eye contact, gaze awareness and movement, body language, and sound. There is no better a place to observe this than at a cocktail party. Watch people scan for visual contact, early warning indicators – friend or foe, supporter or rival. It is all very subtle. Our acoustic performance is more subliminal and no less impressive. Not only can we talk to one person or group and maintain a sensible conversation, but we can scan the room and pick out the voice and words of an individual many feet away. Despite the hubbub of voices, we can often decode the essential nature of what is being said. Machines find this extremely difficult, if not impossible.

All of this happens in meetings and conference rooms too. So the question is: can electronic environments provide these facilities? In a limited way it appears they can. First of all large screens with suitably placed cameras can create the illusion of eye contact. Steerable microphone and speaker arrays can create acoustic differentiation linked to our head position and eye focus. Not quite the cocktail party, but close. This technology might just steer us away from excessive travel. In my experience the only people who like to travel are those who do not do it. So perhaps the most demanding requirement is the change of mindset required.

My childhood had many special places of curiosity and pleasure. In particular, the garden shed, pantry and attic had their own chaos, order, colours and smells. For sheer delight the attic was best. What was it about this collection of dust-covered artifacts that delighted me so? Well it is difficult to define, but certainly a combination of history, belonging, the evoking of lost memories, discovery and perhaps an element of voyeurism. In the attic you can discover your history and that of your family.

Today many PCs parallel the attic, with their guardians loath to allow anyone direct access to the hard disk or screen. Until they are in trouble and need help, they guard access with the same diligence they afford their wardrobe or home. However, when deadlines are fast approaching and nothing is working, then the defences are dropped to give an opportunity for repair. At this point the desire for privacy and security are waived in the interest of survival.

A non-techno-friend recently called me late one evening because his PC was running badly. Apparently it was sluggish, crashing regularly, and had been extremely unreliable for weeks. Now he had reached an impasse and could not work, and his deadline was just 10 hours away, the next morning. So I was firmly invited round to his home and given total access and freedom of action. 'Please, just fix it fast', was the plea.

I started to roam the desktop, which resembled a major motorway accident site with wreckage and fallout extending well into the hard disk. What a mess, how did it ever work? Movie files and documents had been placed inside preference folders and other obscure files inside the operating system; applications had found their way into working folders;

files and objects had been duplicated with multiple copies in diverse locations. And worse, at a first scan, over 30 per cent of the hard disk appeared to be chaotically occupied by junk.

Sitting with my friend, and feeling slightly uncomfortable, I started the clean-up process. Junking, erasing filing, renaming, replacing files, folders and objects. Nothing was safe as I trashed over 50Mbytes. The next step was to place all the working files into a folder, and co-locate all the applications. After an hour I felt ready to run the diagnostic pack, and we took a break for coffee whilst it did its stuff. An hour later the PC was debugged, defragged, and running sweeter than ever before.

During the clean-up process I had gently asked questions to try to figure out how this PC had got into such a mess, and became progressively clear that my non-techno-friend had no idea. It was all a complete mystery; a PC was just a magic box that did stuff; and outcomes were often a surprise or shock.

A few days later I opened my laptop and started my routine cull of old files and messages. Perhaps it was the memory of my friend's PC, or childhood attic, that prompted me to examine my applications and operating system. I started to delete, or place items into a 'Not Used' folder. Stickies, scrap book, numerous print drivers, modem scripts, wizards, art folders, voices, acres of fonts, non-English options and much more were deleted or isolated. Having cleaned out this IT attic I found the machine booted up and operated faster, and suffered fewer spurious delays and lock-ups. As I continued progressively to delete soft-junk, some applications were trimmed down to 30 per cent of their original size, and I realised I might have found a Network Computer in the attic.

*With that
(computing)
science, we are
entering an era
of exhaustivity,
which is also an
era of
exhaustion.*
Jean Baudrillard,
1987

The expansion in software size and complexity is now over-taking the remarkable advances in computer hardware speed and storage density. A sustained doubling of hardware capabilities every 12 to 18 months since 1960 seems to be no match for applications that required 0.5Mbyte of RAM 10 years ago, and now demand well over 5Mbyte. So today we have Power PCs apparently running slower than a 386 of only a few years ago. What is happening? Has the software industry lost control? Will it continue just to consume all future hardware gains; ignore optimisation; and provide ever more complex and unwanted facilities embedded in more and more lines of code?

At the present rate of software expansion we will soon need a super-computer to write an office memo. And it is not just PC-related software; it is almost universally true of all commercial, defence and engineering systems – software just keeps expanding. It is as if we have learned nothing from our decades of working with hardware. Superficially, the engineering differences between hardware and software now seem minimal, and the cost of software manufacture is often greater. So why do we not optimise and worry about software cost and efficiency?

Could it be that software is something so new and complex that it will defy all our efforts at analysis and formalism? Or is it just that we never before had problems with hundreds and thousands of loops and I/O functions? If this is the case we could be in a new realm of the unknowable, well beyond our mental capacity to decode. So what are we to do? Of course we can continue on our present course and suffer a continuing, and probably terminal, slow-down. Alternatively, we can pin our hopes on new programming

111

languages such as Java that are tighter, smarter and better organised. Perhaps these will see us take the vital step to software building blocks that can be glued together in an understandable and efficient manner.

In the physical world, we built bridges of wood and stone and steel, investigated the material properties, and later discovered molecules and atoms. In the software world we seem to have started with the electrons and have yet to discover molecules, let alone the concept of wood, stone and steel. We currently lack any suitable abstractions to form a systematic view, and we know nothing of the general properties. Software modules, discrete building blocks, might be the fix we need. However, progress in this direction has been very slow and there may be a new alternative.

Developments in artificial life systems now see genetic mutation and exchange creating a different richness of solutions. Software that writes itself similarly to the evolutionary process of life is now a crude reality. Control systems requiring millions of lines of code have been replaced by less than a thousand evolutionary lines, and purists now worry about not understanding the way the machines do it. But the truth is we are not particularly clever about understanding how we do it either; the complexity is generally well beyond a single human mind. So here is a new world of machine-generated code, where they programme and learn, and we unknowingly use the tools produced. Most impressively, the machines may soon watch us, learn from our habits as they change and continually modify the code to meet our requirements. A society of new minds, perhaps.

For the most part people do not understand people, and people do not understand machines. The big question is, will machines understand machines and people? I hope so. It would be a great breakthrough to get some understanding into software.

People will soon get tired of staring at a plywood box every night.

D.F. Zanuck, Head of 20th Century Fox, 1946

Apart from the addition of more scanning lines, colour and a larger screen size, television has changed little since the 1930s. It remains dominated by the cathode ray tube and is a limited and largely passive two-dimensional medium. For a true technological leap forward we have to go well beyond the current industry desire to sell us higher definition (even more lines), bigger, wider screens and more channels.

We are moving towards a world of everything on demand; information, interaction, and experience through visual and acoustic immersion. TV technology can deliver much of this to the home and office by the coalescing of computers and communications. In a first step in this direction we see Video on Demand services being tested in trials worldwide. Here the viewer could ultimately have access to all the video material imaginable, with extensions into shopping, museums, art galleries, libraries, medicine, care, education – into the complete world of information.

For any chance of success, it is essential that the user interface surpasses the dreaded VHS controller, or for that matter the PC. If this is not the case we shall see a high proportion of the population effectively frozen out of this information future. Making information available to anyone aged between 3 and 90 is the great challenge – the technology has to be humanised. The way in which this is being addressed has already moved beyond the Graphical User Interface (GUI) to the Shopping Mall, street, store or library paradigm. Here the user moves into familiar surroundings with information access framed as a real, rather than artificial, electronic book; a furniture store instead of a catalogue; travel agent instead of a brochure. In such an environment you have nothing to learn as all is familiar and intuitive.

Beyond the interface we will be confronted by a vast choice with thousands of virtual shops and stores across the planet. Selecting a programme from a choice of a few tens of channels is manageable, a few hundreds is difficult, but 10,000 is impossible. This can be overcome with artificial intelligence primed to learn our changing interest profile. Such a system could even provide a degree of serendipity as it learns about us, and offers opportunities to see this or that film, purchase this or that watch, tie, dress, shirt, etc. An electronically generated short-form preview – the essence of the film, or opportunity, compressed into a few minutes – is already possible.

For a significant step beyond all of this we have to move to immersive systems with large (wall size) flat-panel, head- or eye-mounted displays – a saturation of the visual, acoustic, and ultimately the tactile to realise total interaction. With such technology we will no longer be spectators, but participants, part of the feature film, totally involved. This might seem far fetched, but there is nothing here that has not already been tried in research laboratories.

A more immediate and available technology employs miniature TV cameras mounted at eye level, with microphones above the ears – a surrogate head. The output of this device can be coupled to a VR headset. So, if you wear the VR headset, and I the surrogate head, then you effectively stand inside me looking out. What I see you see; what I hear you hear, and soon – what I feel you will feel. Why be limited to two people when we can broadcast to millions? In the 21st century perhaps we will all go to the Olympic Games without leaving home, and we may stop watching and start participating.

It's like driving a car at night. You never see further than your headlights, but you can make the whole trip that way.

E.L. Doctorow, 1988

Mankind's progress is critically dependent on each generation's ability to stand on the creative shoulders of those before. Throwing rocks at prey gave away to the spear, the bow and arrow, and ultimately guns. But on the way we invented the lathe, milling machine and grinder to spin off even more inventions and products. The process of protection through patents came late in the day and served to promote rather than stem the inventive stream and progress. And so the thermionic valve gave way to the transistor, integrated circuit and the vast array of new technologies we enjoy today.

Intellectual property is also protected by copyright, which was originally concerned with authorship and prose. This ancient paradigm has now moved into the world of software and is both an impediment to progress and the subject of confusion. It seems reasonable that a book should be protected against plagiarism and banditry, but software is different. Here we have an interactive and creative space where elements can be mapped from one system or function to another. No one would consider making individual nuts and bolts anymore – we just buy them by the box. Well, software is available in boxes too, but it comes with a copyright restriction. This often means no copying or modification under any circumstances, and almost certainly no access to the source code.

The same is true of content. From music to video and animation, copyright now serves to restrict rather than promote use, and worse, serves to stem invention. The old world was about producing a few things and selling them at high prices; the new is enabling the converse, selling very large numbers at very low prices. It is about assembling readily available and networked components, adding new and original material, and rapidly advancing the art. Copyright is stemming this positive feedback process that served the progress of hardware so well. In effect, software copyright often means having to make every nut, bolt and screw as if they could not be replicated or mass produced.

Ideally a new regime is needed, a fresh approach that is neither copyright nor patent in the old sense; something that can deal with a networked world where copying is so tempting and easy, and effective policing almost impossible. In the past, copyright made everyone criminals by default as they recorded radio and TV material off air. Now people are tempted by the sharing of games, applications and programs. For sure, a human software police force and teams of lawyers are not the solution, but electronic agents and operating bombs might be. Attaching agents to software that flag intrusion, modification and use to the originator are simple to realise in a networked world. The fire-wall of the floppy, CD and snail mail may only require the inclusion of warning flags and by-use self-destruct or corrupting mechanisms.

Ultimately, the solution may fall solely with the originators and users of code, with no need for the attention of outside agencies. Technology has now reached a point where it can take care of itself without human intervention. Our interests would be best served if we concentrated on encouraging the propagation and use of software to create an increasingly rich and growing field of content. Software and content could then beget even more, as positive feedback would take full reign. The old and outmoded quill pen copyright mentality will serve only to restrict the fundamental mechanisms of progress – standing on the shoulders of others. As my old university professor once observed: borrowing one man's results is plagiarism, but borrowing from ten is research.

116

The idea that information can be stored in a changing world without an overwhelming depreciation of its value is false.

Norbert Wiener, 1950

The benefits of going digital are manifest in the infinite varieties, malleability, reproducibility, transmission switching, routing and storage potential of all forms of data. In theory, once we have captured text, images, movies, sound files, simulations and models they can be stored forever without degradation of the original form, and be copied or transmitted anywhere free from distortion. These, then, are the key differentiators with the earlier and far more volatile world of analogue information. But there is also a hidden facet, and that is the economic benefit which came with the ability to manufacture the transistor and integrated circuit. Even though it requires far greater complexity, realising almost anything in digital form is generally far lower cost than analogue in terms of repeatability and mass production. All of this was apparent in the early 1960s when the digital revolution began and it more or less remains the case today. So we have a digital telephone network, LANs, Internet, copper, optical fibre, radio and satellites transporting information across the planet in an almost seamless fashion. For real-time speech and moving pictures, any bit loss is managed down to a point where it is imperceptible. For financial and other data, great care is taken to ensure a zero bit error transfer. All this works and is accepted, and the digital world now dominates.

Why then do I find a slow degradation of images and other digitally stored material; what is going wrong? It appears that uncontrolled and unseen transformations now pose a threat. At the simplest level, just try to access digitally stored documents from 10 years ago. First, the original application may have disappeared or have been replaced by something more advanced that will not read, or changes the format of, the data. Second, the reader hardware may be in a museum, or you may not have the correct fonts, characters, lines and colour pallet, but the data might still be there and ultimately accessible. More difficult is the storage disc that has been corrupted by stray fields, read-write errors, or just natural magnetic decay. Floppy and hard disks are far from perfect, and they do deteriorate with time.

On a more subtle and unseen level we have digital format transformations where information is destroyed and lost forever. This can be as rudimentary as formatting information between applications. Image processing is a prime example with bit mapping to and from a limited choice colour palette and definition. Once an image has changed down from thousands of colours to 256, from 32 to 16 bit, and so on, there is no way back, information has been lost forever. Cascade through several digital transforms and the damage is usually all too obvious.

Coding presents a more subtle mechanism for information loss. Squeezing data into ever tighter storage spaces and narrower transmission channels can see a progressive distortion that becomes amplified by repeated concatenation of such lossy processes. It is often the case that zero loss coding processes are only 'almost zero' in reality. In the fast moving world of technology, advances in coding algorithms now parallel those in applications. If you repeatedly move your information between machines, applications and operating systems, don't be surprised at a fading digital illusion.

Perhaps we should not be surprised by this outturn of our digital technology. Somewhere on the planet there will be a virgin copy of what we lose or corrupt, a bit like the printing plate held by the Royal Mint so the currency in our pocket can be updated. For now, however, I'm putting my trust in a CD burner.

M51 REBOOT TRIGGERS

At a recent air show I observed a young man sitting in the cockpit of a modern fighter aircraft excitedly talking to the pilot about the design, performance and instrumentation. The pilot seemed impressed by the knowledge this potential protégé had gained through flight simulation packages. Soon they moved onto the weapons system and the clutch of buttons and triggers clustered on the head of the joystick. To the young man's surprise there was an extra trigger for no obvious purpose. The pilot revealed it to be the software reboot trigger. Yep, they actually reboot software mid-flight, during battle, and sometimes more than once.

So here was a $40m machine with flaky software. I tried to get more detail and was told that it was not uncommon and did not constitute a primary risk or degrade the machines' flying ability. But I couldn't help wondering about other defence systems, civil aircraft, nuclear reactors and my car. Yes, my PC can lock up from time to time, but please, not my engine management system. I already have a car hi-fi with a mind of its own and no reboot mechanism. The garage is trying its best to fix it, but the only way to reboot is to disconnect the battery. Soon I shall resort to cutting into the wiring harness to install a trigger on my gear lever. Come to think of it, perhaps that is what those pilots had done.

Looking back to my childhood I recall when most technology was unreliable; the radio, TV, record player, cameras, clocks, wristwatches and electricity supply, in fact everything, was flaky. Driving a car 50 miles was a major expedition, and switching the radio on was a bit chancy too. All of these technologies have now changed to become phenomenally reliable, but it has taken over 100 years of commercial development, competitive markets and consumer pressure to achieve. Mechanical, electromechanical, electrical, electronic and production engineering have come a very long way, as have the design and manufacturing process. More notably, our requirements for quality in everyday technology have also risen dramatically; we now demand it.

In contrast, popular software for the masses has been around for only a couple of decades, and as an industry it lacks any real competition. Packages tend to be unique, non-interoperable and non-interchangeable, and there are no common operating platforms or systems. Moreover, software continues to be developed at a pace that keeps us dazzled by the diversity and abundance. Although this new tool and medium is vital to our future progress and prosperity, it is generally unstable and likely to remain so for at least another decade.

However, among some classes of software and systems there are signs of a growing stability. Watches, calculators, pagers, mobile phones, washing machines, dishwashers and other small contained systems have perhaps come to the end of an evolutionary road and are stable. Thankfully, engine management, TV and hi-fi systems are also in this category. But large systems like the PC present major difficulties. Loading new applications and upgrading software still makes you hold your breath. When will this situation change? Only when there is sufficient competition, uniformity, compatibility, and we complain enough, and have the option to vote with our feet.

Network computing might just be the opportunity we need to bring about the necessary change. A universal operating system and language with an effective infinity of vendors may be on the horizon. Then we might get a universal and basic word processor, graphics package, spreadsheet, mail, plug and play, and much more, all of it honed up and non-flaky, with no reboot triggers.

Time is a waste
of money.
Oscar Wilde,
1894

Only 15 years ago, using computers and making telephone calls was something of an ordeal. The processing speed of computers and printers meant you could wait for seconds or minutes for screen-fill or print-out. For telephone users the concatenated electromechanical switching delays meant you could wait over 30 seconds after dialling the last digit (remember those old mechanical dials?) before you heard any ring or engaged tone. How different today. Now we get irritated if we do not hear a ring tone immediately we press the last digit on the keypad, or when we have to wait seconds for a PC application to load. The generic problem is having to wait for a period that is too short to do anything else, but long enough to break our concentration. Delays of a fraction of a second disrupt our mental agility and interactive creativity to an alarming degree.

In contrast we now have an abundance of bandwidth, storage capacity and processing power, with optical fibre and Power PCs. Moreover, technology promises even higher levels of circuit density and clock speed at insignificant cost. We are thus approaching the realisation of a dream: to access everything, everywhere, any time, within 3 clicks of a mouse and have screen-fill and interaction within a second. For us to enjoy natural, and effective, communication with people and machines, in real or virtual worlds, the need is for sensory delays of less than 100ms.

Why foster such a dream? The principal reasons are twofold: firstly, we live in an accelerating world where we all have to do more in less time and delays limit our creativity and output; secondly, it can be done. Trying to interact with anything, or anyone, at less than natural human speed is counterproductive and irritating. Try a telephone call over a geostationary satellite, which introduces over 300ms of delay, and it is obvious. An even more obvious experience is that of trying to access information from the Internet – the Information Super Cart Track. Here delay is endemic due to inappropriate protocols and layers of unnecessary and inefficient software. Even writing a letter, sending e-mail and manipulating simple documents now seem to require a Power PC to get delays down to a few seconds. The reality is many applications waste increasing Mbytes of RAM making the front end prettier, and providing unwanted and unused facilities, rather than making the process more slick and effective.

Deregulated telecoms markets may soon see the concatenation of digital mobile telephones (with an internal codec delay in excess of 120ms), statistical multiplexers, ATM switches, satellite and cable links of numerous unco-ordinated suppliers adding undefined transmission delays. This new regime of unpredictable delays will take us further away from realising another dream: matching man and machine to achieve effective and efficient communication and creativity. But perhaps most dangerous is the prospect of economic routings chosen in ignorance of the final application. E-mail is never a problem, but speech with a total coding and transmission delay of more than 0.5s would be a disaster.

Just watch children interact with machines and it is immediately apparent that they have an insatiable desire for instant gratification – the shortest response time and best graphics. Looking at professionals you see the same phenomena – a desire to be able to do more, faster. All the technology required is available today; we only have to adopt the right mindset and implement the solutions. In the meantime, I suspect our progress will continue to be frustrated by the delays of systems, computers and software configured for the past.

complex systems

intelligence

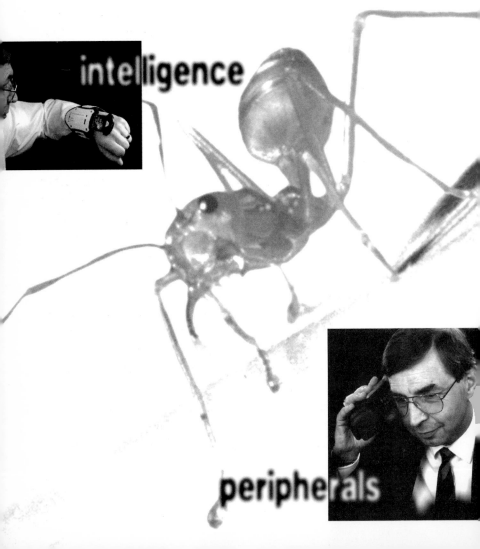

peripherals

Tralfamadorians, of course, say that every creature and planet in the Universe is a machine. It amuses them that so many Earthlings are offended by the idea of being machines.

Kirt Vonnegut, Star Trek

Self-organisation and chaos are vital ingredients for all carbon-based life. Every living thing exists on the edge of a strange attractor, just a hair's breadth from death, in a risky, fit for purpose, non-linear world of weak hierarchies, a world where simple rules predicate complex behaviour. Here uncertainty, competition, mutation and reproduction are key to survival and progress. Unless life lives on the edge, it does not live at all. So far, these principles have not been applied to engineered systems which are largely linear, optimised, strongly hierarchical, non-competitive, and minimise risk through large safety margins and free energy.

It is curious that we are moving in a direction of creating ever more complex software to perform essentially simple tasks. In contrast, nature does the converse, generating unbelievably complex behaviour from incredibly simple software. The difference, of course, is the millions of years nature has been allowed to get it right. We, on the other hand, face much shorter timescales. But, simple life systems – worms, ants and bees – have been simulated on modest computers realising the major interactions in nests and communities. Some of this work has now moved to practical application as control software for networks and information agents.

While the underlying software for each entity may be only a few hundred lines of easily understood code, the emergent behaviour of a society of such entities is another matter. This generally defies prediction and is full of surprises. It might just be that systems of this type cannot be engineered from the standpoint of our established methods and principles. We may have to let go of our long-held desire to define and constrain all the outcomes by specifying, designing and testing systems.

Exponentially growing communication, mobility and information working is creating an increasingly chaotic world. The notion that everything can be controlled, ordered and specified in a manner reminiscent of the early days of the telephone is a grave error. No matter how many people are employed, there will never be enough. Systems will not be able to keep up with the developments of applications, peripheral devices, and new modes of human-machine interdiction.

Taking a leaf out of nature's book, it is clear that we will increasingly need evolutionary systems to meet chaotic demand. Genetics, sex, mutation and progeny spring to mind, but we cannot afford to wait for millions of years of chance mutation. Looking at carbon systems we see a world dominated by one- and two-sex systems. Two sexes are the most adaptable, complex and intelligent. So we might suppose that sex in software, with the super speed of machines, might suffice. But should we be constrained by nature as to the mechanism and numbers involved, or indeed the nature of the progeny? Probably not. In software there are no constraints whatsoever. Morality and society do not exist to constrain the riches of behaviour.

We might envisage a silicon world where a learned and positive behaviour is passed on from one generation to another. Progeny by instalments might be a new means of avoiding the evolutionary cul-de-sacs that hamper carbon. When you have evolved to become an elephant you cannot backtrack to become mouse, no matter how many generations you wait. Progeny by piece parts, many offspring glued together to make the whole, may then provide a solution.

When all of this comes together with noisy decision-making, a subtle blending of random uncertainty and chaos, instead of the full determinism of nailed down logic and software, we may have the right conditions for silicon life.

The question is: are we smart enough to spot artificial life when it spontaneously erupts?

Do not be bullied by authoritative pronouncements about what machines will never do. Such statements are based on pride, not fact.

Marvin Minsky, MIT, 1982

For some years, top of the range copiers and other office machinery have had enough built-in intelligence to call for maintenance help through a self-dial telephone call. Such intelligence is now being extended to the garage forecourt for the replenishment of fuel, detection of spillages and maintenance of pumping equipment. Automatic calls for replenishment of food- and commodity-dispensing machines at airports, stations and in the high street are a more recent development. The logistic advantages of this technology are subtle and significant. Only visiting sites when necessary saves time, resources and money, but topping up machines in response to exceptional demand means sales opportunities are not missed. Drinks machines sell more when it is hot, and are soon emptied by local events that are hard to predict, such as flight and train delays and traffic jams. In the not too distant future we might expect this capability to be an integral part of homes, appliances, cars and body-worn devices.

Most of us already wear a remarkable range of electronics in the form of watches, pagers, calculators and mobile phones. The office we wear, which integrates all of these functions with computing power, may not be so far away, and with it will come the added bonus of remote health-monitoring in real time.

In the UK today, 2 per cent of the population are diabetic, and even more are on some form of drug treatment. Ideally these people require constant monitoring and care to meet their needs, representing a significant workload for the healthcare system. As technology extends our longevity, and the birth rate declines, we face a future of increasing numbers of dependent people, and a diminishing number of carers. In the 21st century, providing the level of care that we enjoy today will be inconceivable. We will have an older population and far fewer people working and creating wealth, so some new technological solutions will be necessary.

With future wearable electronics it is feasible that the fundamental monitoring of heart, respiration, blood pressure, skin, salinity, blood glucose and other characteristics can be provided in real time. Such features could become a part of the office you wear, coupled to algorithms that maintain the right balance of insulin through an artificial pancreas, or drug balance through automatic dispensers. But it does not stop here. What about the technology that wears us? The number of internal body part replacements is accelerating and they are increasingly electronic, or mechatronic in form. It is inconceivable that we could give copying machines the intelligence to call for help when they are about to fail, and then neglect the pacemaker or artificial heart on which so many people are dependent for their very existence.

In the research laboratories of the world there are already prototype artificial replacements for the pancreas, the liver, the kidneys, the inner ear and other vital organs. So we are faced with the prospect of larger numbers of people becoming a little less human and a little more cyborg. In the ultimate analysis my 7-year-old son spotted the really obvious. Today we have donor cards for all real human tissue parts replacement. Being hit by a bus, or suddenly dying from whatever cause, means that you and I can leave vital organs for the immediate use of disadvantaged people who are still alive. The logical extension is that we need a donor card so that our artificial heart, kidneys or other replacement parts may also be recovered and used by others. The ultimate extrapolation really is donor cards for robots.

Sex is a short cut to everything.
Anne Cumming, 1917

Of all the life forms on planet earth only Homo sapiens optimises anything. Buy a saloon car and it may not be optimised for speed, but it will be reliable. Buy a racing car and you get the speed, but then have to worry about reliability. The fact that optimisation, brittleness and reliability go hand in hand is something we learned over thousands of years and now use to great effect. Being able to make reliable and low-cost products is a key plank of our society. In contrast, mother nature only employs fit for purpose; she optimises nothing, and her survival statistics are often very impressive. So, have we missed an engineering trick?

Reliability and reproducibility are key achievements of the industrial age realised through incremental improvements from one generation to the next. This is a powerful and directed evolutionary process where we stand on the shoulders of previous generations and employ cumulative experience and knowledge. It is unlike any mechanism found in nature, and results from hierarchical and structured thinking. Modular design and construction definitely works. If you can make a lathe from a bow and arrow, then you can make a better one with the parts you produce. Similarly, if you can make transistors you can make circuits, and then integrated circuits, and machines that make better transistors. And so positive feedback accelerates the process as machines beget better machines. Mother nature never uses such directed evolution because it requires intelligence – and a god-like hand.

So what of future software systems? Can we expect new engineering processes to emerge? You might think so but perhaps not, as the majority of human thinking is tempered by direct experience of things physical. Also, our limited ability to access non-physical experience might be a key constraint. Just how do you understand 2 million lines of high-level, and very abstract, code? Our mathematical tools and thinking are useless for systems of such scale and complexity, and so we resort to modular designs precluding optimisation and directed evolution. All of this leads to slow response times and poor reliability.

Mother nature understands nothing, and so would not do it this way. She would use blind evolution through natural selection and chance mutation over millions of years. But we cannot afford such development times; we need solutions in weeks. Fortunately, the speed of machines allows us to accelerate the evolution of software entities, so a million years takes less than a week. In carbon life it is the single-sex systems that dominate (flora and fauna), two-sex systems that are the smartest (mammals) and the multiple-sex systems that enjoy the better resilience (insects and fungi). To be really smart also seems to entail enhanced attraction through the mechanisms inherent in sexual reproduction. In software, love has nothing to do with the process; it is cold and calculated with the same regard for survival of the fittest seen in the insect and plant world. But there is now a new card to play. Software can adapt and adopt the right number of sexes to meet the needs of a particular problem. Interestingly, the smartest software evolved to date seems to come from 3 or 4 sexes not 2.

So when we try to predict the future we should remember the lathe and the transistor, and contemplate the feedback impact of rapidly evolving software. Machine intelligence will speed up the process further and will not be hampered by emotion or, for that matter, the mating incompatibilities and sexual limitations of carbon life. But like us, future machines will be concerned with information and disorder processing, only they will be faster and better at it.

131

Undernourished, intelligence becomes like the bloated belly of a starving child: swollen, filled with nothing the body can use.
Andrea Dworkin, 1978

Just what is it that constitutes true intelligence? What is it that apparently elevates us above machines, and perhaps all living things? To date we have no formal definition for intelligence that is universally accepted, tried and proven. Estimating the intelligence of systems sees us resorting to crude computations of neural count, processing speed and connectivity. So we as a species have around 10EXP11 neurons and a 10EXP4 connectivity. Given the uncertainties in getting the numbers right in the first place, that puts us in the 10EXP15 bracket. Now include our synaptic processing rate of around 10 to 100bit/s and some localisation assumptions, and we look like a 1TFlop/s processor. But we know we are much more.

Chances are that our current estimates of our brain capacity are grossly on the low side, if for no other reason than we do not fully understand how our own wetware functions. One obvious factor that does distinguish us from silicon machines, is our relative information I/O rate. For us, information flow is strictly dominated by input rather than output. From the moment we are born until we die our sensory system is feeding our brain vast amounts of information. Our utterances and animation pale into insignificance in raw bit rate terms compared to the visual, audio and tactile input we constantly absorb.

As best as we can estimate, each of our eyes feeds us bits from 127,000,000 rods and cones in the retina, via the visual cortex, at about 1Gbit/s. This far outweighs the infeed from our hearing, tactile, smell and taste sensors which total less than 20Mbit/s. In contrast, our typing rate is only around 40bit/s, speech is about 100bit/s, whilst gesticulation and facial expression are even lower (but of course can be socially encoded to convey far more). A glance from a loved one at a cocktail party, or a close colleague in a meeting, can be worth Mbits.

Contrast all of this with the average PC, or better still, the mainframe. We complain about them being dumb machines, and yet we deprive them of input. For the most part all they get is a diet of low bit rate alpha-numerics. No direct visual and audio feed, and certainly no tactile taste or smell. So they all seem to operate in the mode of creating more output than input. From billing customers, to issuing pay slips, predicting the weather, or controlling a space shot, their input is meagre compared to their output. No wonder they are dumb.

For machines to achieve true intelligence might then require a change of I/O bias. I suspect they will need much more input data, more contemplation processing time, and less time and resources devoted to output. Of all the human kind we revere, it is probably the thinkers who make the greatest impact on mankind's progress. Often they are accused of being non-communicative, but perhaps that is the secret. Deep thought demands concentration and a degree of mental isolation. Input dominates in all such cases, but when the output comes it can be devastating, like $E = mc^2$ for example.

We have within our grasp the basic technologies to build machines that might just be capable of some form of free thinking. What is lacking is a suitably formatted information infeed, a sensory system that will match them into our, and other worlds. Perhaps that is why one famous machine of science fiction came to the conclusion that the answer to an important human question was 42, which is 101010, just a free running clock.

640K *ought to be*
enough for
anybody.
Bill Gates,
1981

Just 12 years ago the computer on my desk had 1Mbyte of RAM and 20Mbytes of disk storage. My word processing package required less than 0.5Mbyte of RAM, and my document store oscillated around 3Mbytes. In fact, most applications at that time, and there were few, consumed somewhere between 0.35 and 0.5Mbytes of RAM. What a contrast today. A top end word processing package requires at least 5Mbytes and can demand as much as 20Mbytes. The same is true of spreadsheet, graphics and animation applications. Moreover, there is an increasing need to have several of these heavyweight applications running at the same time. As I write these 620 words I not only have a word processing application open, but a spreadsheet, graphics package, diary application, mail system and a raft of on-line connections. My computer now has 2.5Gbytes of hard disk and 64Mbytes of RAM. In the same 12-year period, the clock speed has gone from a mere 6 to 120MHz, and curiously the word processor is more sluggish. What have we done?

It is interesting to plot the progress of hardware and software operating speeds and our own perception. While computer hardware platforms are increasingly powerful, roughly doubling in capability every 12 to 18 months, the race to build the world's heaviest aeroplane, by the software industry, sees performance actually getting worse. At the present rate of progress we will require a Cray Super Computer to write a simple office memo by the year 2015. Clearly this trend is not sustainable; it cannot continue. Surely word processing, spreadsheet and graphics packages must have come to the end of the road in terms of their demand for more memory?

From a user point of view, we see a tidal wave of new facilities and extensions. Not surprisingly we now find it increasingly difficult to operate and exploit applications much beyond a few per cent of their full capability. There are no longer any experts; we are all amateurs discovering, day on day, new quirks and features. Our difficulties are further compounded by cosmetic changes that shuffle the location of commands, and appearance of menus and icons, between subsequent versions. On top of all this there are backward and forward compatibility limitations between releases, which provide another layer of frustration.

What is going to be interesting in the next 5 years is the emergence of distributed computing with new Java-based operating systems delivering Applets on demand. Given the constraints of the present telecommunications network, this will automatically dictate that we scroll back 15 years to applications of just a few hundred kbytes when on-line access is required. If we do not, the delays encountered in pulling these down the line will be enormous and will stifle the creation of a world of distributed working. It might be that an alternative world will also emerge where the producers of software sell us a basic word processing package and then we choose to purchase those features that we really need rather than buying all of it. Suddenly we would then become the masters of our own destiny and the constructors of our own applications in a Lego-like software world.

So, will we still need a large amount of RAM and hard disc storage? Very probably. The reasons: the hardware manufacturers seeking to maintain and/or expand their turnover coupled with falling hardware costs. But probably the key driver will be ourselves and our desire to own and hold onto software. We are also moving in a direction of having at least five applications open simultaneously in order to complete increasingly complex tasks. So unless someone starts to integrate the Applets for word processing, graphics, spreadsheet, e-mail, etc. we will remain Mbyte hungry.

stock exchange

trader desk

Stocks have reached what looks like a permanently high plateau.
Irving Fisher,
Yale University,
1929

Only a decade ago just over 170 individual dealing rooms employed thousands in the City of London. Eye contact, face-to-face interaction, telephones, and paper were the media. Few could envisage the death of this system, until the Big Bang of October 1986. The liberalisation of the market and global, computer-based trading left the floors deserted. Screen trading was a revolution that changed the nature of money markets for ever. The first lesson of the Big Bang was predicted by many with just a modest appreciation of system dynamics. Delay and synchronisation in similarly distributed systems, rapidly forces them into limit cycles as delay is diminished. In non-technical terms: trading systems go into a chaotic buy, sell, buy pattern – and delay had to be put back in to restore stability.

In 1986 PhDs were rare in the City, but today dealing systems have become rocket science. The reason: whoever has the best communications, computers, and algorithms has the edge. Despite all their apparent sophistication, the majority of human traders use a decision process that is simple, and amazingly successful. As shares go up, they assume they will continue to go up until they turn down, and then continue to go down until they turn back up again. Couple this with knowledge and intuition, and you have a world-class trader. Computers with algorithms based on this approach are relatively successful, and make money but need more intelligence to compete.

Today's leading edge systems use artificial intelligence to buy and sell across global markets. These algorithms learn from experience and predict what should happen, analyse the results, and adjust to improve. In reality these are simple animals, but then simple animals such as ants are able to achieve remarkable things that humans find impossible. So we may soon see traders being replaced by computers guided by very few people. So far, machines don't commit crimes, rarely make mistakes, are non-emotional, and truly objective. They can work 24 hours a day, 365 days a year, and are totally dedicated. So what might be the next step for the already metaphoric City? Perhaps screen-based trading rooms will also become museums.

If we are working from screens we don't have to be in one room – or be a part of the same company. As in many other sectors, working from home or telecottage is an obvious next step and signals the fragmentation of the industry. To realise such freedom requires us to recognise that we are now witnessing the death of geography, the birth of universal information access, and worldwide round-the-clock working. Instant communication compresses distance, and eradicates time zones. Why do London, Frankfurt, New York, Tokyo all have stock exchanges? In an electronic world they will just be information space, without physical location – the infinite city.

Moving from the trading floor to the electronic dealing room saw a phenomenal shrinkage in people numbers, and change in the skills required. In the next phase it will be the hybrids – the technologist, banker, marketeer, and trader who will lead. And the ultimate question: how clever will we have to be to outstrip automatic trading systems in 20 years' time? Probably more intelligent than our wetware allows. What we perceive as random is often chaotic, and chaotic events have patterns which we are good at spotting. This is the basis of human trading systems. The machines' advantage is their ability to take a wider perspective, recognise short-term patterns faster, and continuously examine the outcomes of all previous moves. In short – they are smarter than us.

*I don't want to
achieve
immortality
through my
work, I want to
achieve it by not
dying
Woody Allen,
1975*

For millennia all our knowledge could easily be contained in one human brain. Father would teach son, mother would teach daughter, each generation adding a little more. It then became necessary to record information on cave walls, clay tablets, skins and parchment. We had reached a critical epoch – all human knowledge could no longer be contained in one brain. Specialism and co-operation were vital; no individual could do everything, compete and survive.

Today, our problem is acute. It is no longer possible to be an expert in anything other than a few virginal topics. For example, just 500 years ago it was possible to be an expert artist, engineer and scientist at the same time. Even 30 years ago it was possible to have a detailed understanding of telecommunication networks, cars, domestic appliances and military systems. Who now understands all of it? No one. Fortunately we do not have to understand the chemistry of a safety match to use one – but someone somewhere does.

Despite specialisation and an exponential growth in knowledge, we still see people of outstanding ability able to understand and contribute more than average. Unfortunately, they die and their expertise is lost for all time. The question is: can we capture their expertise and presence for future generations? Do they have to die 100 per cent?

Multimedia holds out the prospect of being able to capture such wisdom, with the spoken and printed world supported by animated pictures. Suppose as some great teacher gave lectures and interacted one-on-one with students, it was recorded. Over a period of years it is feasible to capture over 95 per cent of all likely questions and debate. How difficult then would it be to construct an artificial persona of this great mind? Might we sit and listen and watch a lecture long after the death and still be able to interact in a meaningful way?

This vision is partially available with today's crude CDs of a mere 630Mbytes capacity, soon to be replaced by the next generation at 8Gbytes. We can already visit the Natural History Museum and receive a description of Barionix or the derivation of the word dinosaur. Granted, the presentation and style are limited by the medium, but it is a first indication of what might be done. Our rudimentary artificial intelligence systems can now filter and assemble the right slices of dialogue. Animation and pictographic representations on demand can also be triggered by a well-phrased question. What is required is a little more intelligence to filter what we require from ill-posed questions or propositions. If only the medium could respond to: 'Describe a dinosaur named Barionix', or 'Was Barionix a dinosaur, and if so, what was it like?'

Just imagine the solution to Fermat's last problem, not scribbled on paper and lost for ever, but recorded for all time; or the many works and ideas of Newton that never saw the light of day. Perhaps, we should go further and contemplate artificial intelligence systems able to access such works, able to coalesce the myriad concepts and results that currently escape us due to our limited human ability and memory. Perhaps, in future, none of us will die in the strict sense, but our essence, an echo of our passing, will live on. Perhaps then we will become a hybrid being, a network of total experience in which learning and understanding are continuously incremented by the inputs and interactions of a peripheral workforce of individual human minds acting in unison with us. At 51 year old, and another decade or two to realise this world, I might just see you there.

Ultimately, literature is nothing but carpentry. With both you are working with reality, a material just as hard as wood.

Gabriel García Márquez, 1985

Not so long ago people would write on both sides of a sheet of paper, and in some cases horizontally and vertically, to make full use of a very expensive and hand-made commodity. Today it seems we can afford to waste paper – or can we? With millions of book titles in print and billions of copies sitting on shelves worldwide, there has to be a finite limit. After all, this is the planet's forests being transformed into thermal insulation and room decoration at the rate of about 250 million tonnes/year. Is this really the right thing to be doing?

No doubt about it, paper is a nice media, and very convenient as it affords zero boot-up time, requires no batteries and can be conveniently folded into a shirt pocket. Relatively speaking, paper is also very low cost as we have become very efficient in its manufacture and reprocessing. In this equation we should not dismiss our individual years of dedication to learning to read and write efficiently. The cost of this skill acquisition is unlikely to be overtaken by the average lifetime of paper consumption we could anticipate enjoying. Perhaps surprisingly, the cost of providing a computer screen for life falls into the same cost bracket as the cost of paper we each consume. This means we are becoming extraordinarily efficient, as working on screen gives at least a tenfold gain over paper-based systems.

Whilst in my work I avoid paper like the plague, and make every effort to avoid printing anything, I still enjoy the look and feel of the occasional book. For non-technical works I am happy to buy a paper or hardback and read in my armchair, but textbooks present a major problem. I can never find one book that covers my topic of study; they are always deficient in one regard or another. What I need is the ability to cook my own. A chapter from here, a paragraph from there, and figures and diagrams from another. Come to think of it, I'd like to do this with music CDs and tapes too. They never have my choice or optimum selection, and cannot be updated and augmented.

Even with no power of content selection and format cooking, I like music stores that let me sample their products before I buy. The old libraries and bookstores were fun too. I used to enjoy being able to browse, sample and choose. But now I would like one more degree of freedom; to download and try on my screen, to modify, add to and compile my own volumes, and then if I really need, to print.

Consider the efficiency of any book you buy – it is hard to exceed 0.02% for a novel and 0.2% for a textbook. Just think how many times you read your individual books, and how many hours they are in your hands during their lifetime. In contrast, and given the ultra-low cost of digital storage, the efficiency of information retention and use on a PC (replaced every three years) is likely to exceed 10%. In my case, I estimate my information storage efficiency to be around 15%. I suspect that if you get past 30 per cent you make some dramatic transition into a new class of human.

As I type this 600 words I am sitting in a forest surrounded by unbounded beauty, trees of all kinds. What are we doing reducing them to pulp just to record our words for a few decades, and to give them the attention of our eyes for an hour or two. I feel kind of comfortable here – among friends.

ABOUT THE AUTHOR

Peter Cochrane BSc, MSc, PhD, DSc, CGIA, FEng, FIEE, FIEEE

Peter Cochrane was born in 1946 and spent his formative years in a mining community in Nottinghamshire where he was educated in the local schools and colleges. He joined the British Post Office at age 16 and spent the first 3 years digging holes, erecting poles and installing cables and telephones. A further 3 years saw him as a linesman and technician maintaining a variety of Strowger, Crossbar and Electronic Switches. Peter then took 5 years out to study electrical engineering at Trent Polytechnic in Nottingham, where he graduated with a BSc Honours in 1973. Later periods at Essex University saw him gain an MSc (1976), PhD (1979) and DSc (1993) in telecommunications and systems engineering. Honorary doctorates from the universities of Essex and Stafford followed in 1996. He is currently a Fellow of the IEE, IEEE and Royal Academy of Engineering, a visiting professor to UCL and Essex universities, and an honorary professor at the University of Kent. In 1986 he received the IEE Electronics Division Premium, in 1994 the Computing and Control Premium and the IERE Benefactors Prize for published papers. In 1994 was also awarded the Marlesham Medal for his personal contribution to the development of fibre-optic systems. Peter has published widely in professional journals, the academic press as well as newspapers and magazines. He is a promoter of science and technology, a regular speaker at conferences and public events, and appears on radio and TV worldwide.

Most of Peter's working life has been spent at BT Laboratories and numerous universities. He has also had extensive experience as a consultant to many international companies, organisations and governments. Since 1973 he

143

has worked on a wide variety of analogue and digital switching and transmission system developments. These have spanned the writing of software, designing components and systems, networks, test equipment, operational and management systems.

After being a group and section manager for 10 years, Peter was promoted to manager of the Long Lines Division in 1978. Here he was involved with intensity modulated and coherent optical systems, photonic amplifiers and wavelength routed networks for terrestrial and undersea applications. He received the Queen's Award for Technology in 1990 as manager for the production of optical receivers for the first Trans-Atlantic undersea optical fibre cable systems. In 1991 he was appointed to head the Systems Research Division which was concerned with future advanced media, computing and communications developments.

A further promotion to head BT Research followed in 1993. In this role Peter recruited and built his present department of 660 people dedicated to the study of future technologies, systems, networks and services. This work has now established new areas of development in human visual, audio and tactile I/O, artificial intelligence and life systems, mobile and wearable computing, econometrics, network and company modelling, network technologies and design. But the biggest concentration, and challenge, has been on matching the inherent abilities of people and technology.

Peter and his wife Brenda live in Suffolk with their two daughters and two sons. When not at work Peter enjoys looking after the family and attempts a wide variety of activities, from DIY, swimming and running, to music and reading. He is also the only senior BT manager who has a skateboard.

INDEX